COLLECTIONS
FOR YOUNG SCHOLARS
VOLUME 5, BOOK I

Learning

Astronomy

Family Heritage

Art by Mary Beth Schwark and Bob Kuester

COLLECTIONS FOR YOUNG SCHOLARS

VOLUME 5, BOOK 1

PROGRAM AUTHORS
Carl Bereiter
Ann Brown
Marlene Scardamalia
Valerie Anderson
Joe Campione

CONSULTING AUTHORS
Michael Pressley
Iva Carruthers
Captain Bill Pinkney

OPEN COURT PUBLISHING COMPANY
CHICAGO AND PERU, ILLINOIS

CHAIRMAN
M. Blouke Carus

PRESIDENT
André W. Carus

EDUCATION DIRECTOR
Carl Bereiter

VICE-PRESIDENT AND PUBLISHER
Barbara Conteh

EXECUTIVE EDITOR
Shirley Graudin

MANAGING EDITOR
Sheelagh McGurn

PROJECT EDITOR
Janette McKenna

ART DIRECTOR
John Grandits

VICE-PRESIDENT, PRODUCTION
AND MANUFACTURING
Chris Vancalbergh

PERMISSIONS COORDINATOR
Diane Sikora

COVER ARTISTS
Mary Beth Schwark
and Bob Kuester

OPEN COURT and ✿ are registered in the U.S. Patent and Trademark Office.
Copyright © 1995 Open Court Publishing Company

Collections for Young Scholars and its representation in calligraphy are registered in the U.S. Patent and Trademark Office.

All rights reserved for all countries. No part of this work may be reproduced or utilized in any form or by any means, electronic or mechanical, including photocopying, recording, or by any information storage or retrieval system, without the written permission of Open Court Publishing Company unless such copying is expressly permitted by federal copyright law. Address requests for permission to reproduce Open Court material to Permissions Coordinator, Open Court Publishing Company, 315 Fifth Street, Peru, IL 61354.

Printed in the United States of America

ISBN 0-8126-5148-0

10 9 8 7 6 5 4 3 2 1

ACKNOWLEDGMENTS

Grateful acknowledgment is given to the following publishers and copyright owners for permission granted to reprint selections from their publications. All possible care has been taken to trace ownership and secure permission for each selection included.

Atheneum Publishers, an imprint of Macmillan Publishing Co.: "Galileo" from *Pioneer Astronomers* by Navin Sullivan, copyright © 1964 by Navin Sullivan.

Bantam Books, a division of Bantam Doubleday Dell Publishing Group, Inc.: "The Night We Started Dancing" by Ann Cameron, from *Free to Be . . . A Family*, by Marlo Thomas and Friends, copyright © 1987 by Free to Be Foundation, Inc.

Curtis Brown, Ltd.: An excerpt entitled "The West Side" from *How Juan Got Home* by Peggy Mann, copyright © 1972 by Peggy Mann.

Chicago Public Library: "To Young Readers" by Gwendolyn Brooks, copyright © 1979 by Gwendolyn Brooks.

Children's Better Health Institute, Benjamin Franklin Literary and Medical Society, Inc.: "Sam at the Library" by Carol Combs Hole, from *Jack and Jill*, copyright © 1967 by Curtis Publishing Co.

Clarion Books, an imprint of Houghton Mifflin Co.: An excerpt from *Voyager to the Planets* by Necia H. Apfel, copyright © 1991 by Necia H. Apfel.

Education Development Center, Inc., Newton, MA: "History of the Tunrit" from *Songs and Stories of the Netsilik Eskimos,* translated by Edward Field from text collected by Knud Rasmussen, illustrated by Kiakshuk and Pudlo, copyright © 1967, 1968 by Education Development Center, Inc.

Farrar, Straus and Giroux, Inc.: An excerpt from *The Heavenly Zoo: Legends and Tales of the Stars,* retold by Alison Lurie, illustrated by Monika Beisner, text copyright © 1979 by Alison Lurie, illustrations copyright © 1979 by Monika Beisner.

Harcourt Brace Jovanovich, Inc.: An excerpt entitled "The Library Card" from *Rufus M.* by Eleanor Estes, illustrated by Louis Slobodkin, copyright 1943 by Eleanor Estes. "Seventh Grade" from *Baseball in April and Other Stories* by Gary Soto, copyright © 1990 by Gary Soto. "Women" from *Revolutionary Petunias and Other Poems* by Alice Walker, copyright © 1970 by Alice Walker.

HarperCollins Publishers: An excerpt entitled "Storks" from *The Wheel on the School* by Meindert DeJong, illustrated by Maurice Sendak, copyright 1954 by Meindert DeJong. An excerpt from *The Land I Lost: Adventures of a Boy in Vietnam* by Huynh Quang Nhuong, text copyright © 1982 by Huynh Quang Nhuong. An excerpt entitled "Chinatown" from *Child of the Owl* by Laurence Yep, copyright © 1977 by Laurence Yep. "Parmele" from *Childtimes: A Three-Generation Memoir* by Eloise Greenfield and Lessie Jones Little, copyright © 1979 by Eloise Greenfield and Lessie Jones Little.

Houghton Mifflin Co.: An excerpt entitled "Into the Light of Day" from *Child of the Silent Night* by Edith Fisher Hunter, copyright © 1963 by Edith Fisher Hunter. An excerpt entitled "Sun and Star Calendars" from *Sky Watchers of Ages Past* by Malcolm E. Weiss, copyright © 1982 by Malcolm E. Weiss. An excerpt entitled "Telescopes" from *The Way Things Work* by David Macaulay, compilation copyright © 1988 by Dorling Kindersley Ltd., London, text copyright © 1988 by David Macaulay and Neil Ardley, illustrations copyright © 1988 by David Macaulay. An excerpt entitled "A Meeting in Space" from *Barbary* by Vonda N. McIntyre, copyright © 1986 by Vonda N. McIntyre. An excerpt from *In Two Worlds: A Yup'ik Eskimo Family* by Aylette Jenness and Alice Rivers, photographs by Aylette Jenness, text copyright © 1989 by Aylette Jenness and Alice Rivers, photographs copyright © 1989 by Aylette Jenness.

Lothrop, Lee & Shepard, a division of William Morrow and Co., Inc.: An excerpt from *Do Bananas Chew Gum?* by Jamie Gilson, text copyright © 1980 by Jamie Gilson.

Macmillan Publishing Co., a division of Macmillan, Inc.: An excerpt entitled "Mukasa at School" from *Mukasa* by John Nagenda, copyright © 1973 by John Nagenda, copyright © 1973 by The Macmillan Co.

Elsa Marston: "Circles, Squares and Daggers: How Native Americans Watched the Skies" by Elsa Marston, copyright © 1990 by Elsa Marston.

continued on page 368

LEARNING

❦

🐦 7 🐦

ASTRONOMY

FAMILY
HERITAGE

❧ *10* ❧

LEARNING

THE LIBRARY CARD

from RUFUS M. by Eleanor Estes
illustrated by Louis Slobodkin

R ufus M. That's the way Rufus wrote his name on his heavy arithmetic paper and on his blue-lined spelling paper. Rufus M. went on one side of the paper. His age, seven, went on the other. Rufus had not learned to write his name in school, though that is one place for learning to write. He had not learned to write his name at home either, though that is another place for learning to write.

The place where he had learned to write his name was the library, long ago before he ever went to school at all. This is the way it happened.

One day when Rufus had been riding his scooter up and down the street, being the motorman, the conductor, the passengers, the steam, and the whistle of a locomotive, he came home and found Joey, Jane, and Sylvie, all reading in the front yard. Joey and Jane were sitting on the steps of the porch and Sylvie was sprawled in the hammock, a book in one hand, a chocolate-covered peppermint in the other.

Rufus stood with one bare foot on his scooter and one on the grass and watched them. Sylvie read the fastest. This was natural since she was the oldest. But Joey turned the pages almost as fast and Jane went lickety-cut on the good parts.

They were all reading books and he couldn't even read yet. These books they were reading were library books. The library must be open today. It wasn't open every day, just a few days a week.

"I want to go to the library," said Rufus. "And get a book," he added.

"We all just came home from there," said Jane, while Joey and Sylvie merely went on reading as though Rufus had said nothing. "Besides," she added, "why do you want a book anyway? You can't even read yet."

This was true and it made Rufus mad. He liked to do everything that they did. He even liked to sew if they were sewing. He never thought whether sewing was for girls only or not. When he saw Jane sewing, he asked Mama to let him sew too. So Mama tied a thread to the head of a pin and Rufus poked that in and out of a piece of goods. That's the way he sewed. It looked like what Jane was doing and Rufus was convinced that he was sewing too, though he could not see much sense in it.

Now here were the other Moffats, all with books from the library. And there were three more books stacked up on the porch that looked like big people's books without pictures. They were for Mama no doubt. This meant that he was the only one here who did not have a book.

"I want a book from the library," said Rufus. A flick of the page as Sylvie turned it over was all the answer he got. It seemed to Rufus as though even Catherine-the-cat gave him a scornful glance because he could not read yet and did not have a book.

Rufus turned his scooter around and went out of the yard. Just wait! Read? Why, soon he'd read as fast if not faster than they did. Reading looked easy. It was just flipping pages. Who couldn't do that?

Rufus thought that it was not hard to get a book out of the library. All you did was go in, look for a book that you liked, give it to the lady to punch, and come home with it. He knew where the library was for he had often gone there with Jane and some of the others. While Jane went off to the shelves to find a book, he and Joey played the game of Find the Duke in the Palmer Cox Brownie books. This was a game that the two boys had made up. They would turn the pages of one of the Brownie books, any of them, and try to be the first to spot the duke, the brownie in the tall hat. The library lady thought that this was a noisy game, and said she wished they would not play it there. Rufus hoped to bring a Brownie book home now.

"Toot-toot!" he sang to clear the way. Straight down Elm Street was the way to the library; the same way that led to Sunday School, and Rufus knew it well. He liked sidewalks that were white the best for he could go the fastest on these.

"Toot-toot!" Rufus hurried down the street. When he arrived at the library, he hid his scooter in the pine trees that grew under the windows beside the steps. Christmas trees, Rufus called them. The ground was covered with brown pine needles and they were soft to walk upon. Rufus always went into the library the same way. He climbed the stairs, encircled the light on the granite arm of the steps, and marched into the library.

Rufus stepped carefully on the strips of rubber matting that led to the desk. This matting looked like dirty licorice. But it wasn't licorice. He knew because once when Sylvie had brought him here when he was scarcely more than three he had tasted a torn corner of it. It was not good to eat.

The library lady was sitting at the desk playing with some cards. Rufus stepped off the matting. The cool, shiny floor felt good to his bare feet. He went over to the shelves and luckily did find one of the big Palmer Cox Brownie books there. It would be fun to play the game of Find the Duke at home. Until now he had played it only in the library. Maybe Jane or Joe would play it with him right now. He laughed out loud at the thought.

"Sh-sh-sh, quiet," said the lady at the desk.

Rufus clapped his chubby fist over his mouth. Goodness! He had forgotten where he was. Do not laugh or talk out loud in the library. He knew these rules. Well, he didn't want to stay here any longer today anyway. He wanted to read at home with the others. He took the book to the lady to punch.

She didn't punch it though. She took it and she put it on the table behind her and then she started to play cards again.

"That's my book," said Rufus.

"Do you have a card?" the lady asked.

Rufus felt in his pockets. Sometimes he carried around an old playing card or two. Today he didn't have one.

"No," he said.

"You'll have to have a card to get a book."

"I'll go and get one," said Rufus.

The lady put down her cards. "I mean a library card," she explained kindly. "It looks to me as though you are too little to have a library card. Do you have one?"

"No," said Rufus. "I'd like to though."

"I'm afraid you're too little," said the lady. "You have to write your name to get one. Can you do that?"

Rufus nodded his head confidently. Writing. Lines up and down. He'd seen that done. And the letters that Mama had tied in bundles in the closet under the stairs were covered with writing. Of course he could write.

"Well, let's see your hands," said the lady.

Rufus obligingly showed this lady his hands, but she did not like the look of them. She cringed and clasped her head as though the sight hurt her.

"Oh!" she gasped. "You'll just have to go home and wash them before we can even think about joining the library and borrowing books."

This was a complication upon which Rufus had not reckoned. However, all it meant was a slight delay. He'd wash his

hands and then he'd get the
book. He turned and went
out of the library, found
his scooter safe among
the Christmas trees, and
pushed it home. He sur-
prised Mama by asking
to have his hands
washed. When this
was done, he mounted
his scooter again and
returned all the long way to
the library. It was not just a little trip to the
library. It was a long one. A long one and a hot one on a day
like this. But he didn't notice that. All he was bent on was
getting his book and taking it home and reading with the others on the front porch. They were all still there, brushing flies
away and reading.

Again Rufus hid his scooter in the pine trees, encircled the
light, and went in.

"Hello," he said.

"Well," said the lady. "How are they now?"

Rufus had forgotten he had had to wash his hands. He
thought she was referring to the other Moffats. "Fine," he said.

"Let me see them," she said, and she held up her hands.

Oh! His hands! Well, they were all right, thought Rufus,
for Mama had just washed them. He showed them to the lady.
There was a silence while she studied them. Then she shook
her head. She still did not like them.

"Ts, ts, ts!" she said. "They'll have to be cleaner than that."

Rufus looked at his hands. Supposing he went all the way home and washed them again, she still might not like them. However, if that is what she wanted, he would have to do that before he could get the Brownie book . . . and he started for the door.

"Well now, let's see what we can do," said the lady. "I know what," she said. "It's against the rules but perhaps we can wash them in here." And she led Rufus into a little room that smelled of paste where lots of new books and old books were stacked up. In one corner was a little round sink and Rufus washed his hands again. Then they returned to the desk. The lady got a chair and put a newspaper on it. She made Rufus stand on this because he was not big enough to write at the desk otherwise.

Then the lady put a piece of paper covered with a lot of printing in front of Rufus, dipped a pen in the ink well and gave it to him.

"All right," she said. "Here's your application. Write your name here."

All the writing Rufus had ever done before had been on big pieces of brown wrapping paper with lots of room on them. Rufus had often covered those great sheets of paper with his own kind of writing at home. Lines up and down.

But on this paper there wasn't much space. It was already covered with writing. However, there was a tiny little empty space and that was where Rufus must write his name, the lady said. So, little space or not, Rufus confidently grasped the pen with his left hand and dug it into the paper. He was not accustomed to pens, having always worked with pencils until now, and he made a great many holes and blots and scratches.

"Gracious," said the lady. "Don't bear down so hard! And why don't you hold it in your right hand?" she asked, moving the pen back into his right hand.

Rufus started again scraping his lines up and down and all over the page, this time using his right hand. Wherever there was an empty space he wrote. He even wrote over some of the print for good measure. Then he waited for the lady, who had gone off to get a book for some man, to come back and look.

"Oh," she said as she settled herself in her swivel chair, "is that the way you write? Well . . . it's nice, but what does it say?"

"Says Rufus Moffat. My name."

Apparently these lines up and down did not spell Rufus Moffat to this lady. She shook her head.

"It's nice," she repeated. "Very nice. But nobody but you knows what it says. You have to learn to write your name better than that before you can join the library."

Rufus was silent. He had come to the library all by himself, gone back home to wash his hands, and come back because he wanted to take books home and read them the way the others did. He had worked hard. He did not like to think he might have to go home without a book.

The library lady looked at him a moment and then she said quickly before he could get himself all the way off the big chair, "Maybe you can *print* your name."

Rufus looked at her hopefully. He thought he could write better than he could print, for his writing certainly looked to him exactly like all grown people's writing. Still he'd try to print if that was what she wanted.

The lady printed some letters on the top of a piece of paper. "There," she said. "That's your name. Copy it ten times and then we'll try it on another application."

Rufus worked hard. He worked so hard the knuckles showed white on his brown fist. He worked for a long, long time, now with his right hand and now with his left. Sometimes a boy or a girl came in, looked over his shoulder and watched, but he paid no attention. From time to time the lady studied his work and she said, "That's fine. That's fine." At last she said, "Well, maybe now we can try." And she gave him another application.

All Rufus could get, with his large generous letters, in that tiny little space where he was supposed to print his name, was R-U-F. The other letters he scattered here and there on the card. The lady did not like this either. She gave him still another blank. Rufus tried to print smaller and this time he got RUFUS in the space, and also he crowded an M at the end. Since he was doing so well now the lady herself printed the *offat* part of Moffat on the next line.

"This will have to do," she said. "Now take this home and ask your mother to sign it on the other side. Bring it back on

Thursday and you'll get your card."

Rufus's face was shiny and streaked with dirt where he had rubbed it. He never knew there was all this work to getting a book. The other Moffats just came in and got books. Well, maybe they had had to do this once too.

Rufus held his hard-earned application in one hand and steered his scooter with the other. When he reached home Joey, Jane and Sylvie were not around any longer. Mama signed his card for him, saying, "My! So you've learned how to write!"

"Print," corrected Rufus.

Mama kissed Rufus and he went back out. The lady had said to come back on Thursday, but he wanted a book today. When the other Moffats came home, he'd be sitting on the top step of the porch, reading. That would surprise them. He smiled to himself as he made his way to the library for the third time.

Once his application blew away. Fortunately, it landed in a thistle bush and did not get very torn. The rest of the way Rufus clutched it carefully. He climbed the granite steps to the library again only to find that the big round dark brown doors were closed. Rufus tried to open them but he couldn't. He knocked at the door, even kicked it with his foot, but there was no answer. He pounded on the door but nobody came.

A big boy strode past with his newspapers. "Hey, kid," he said to Rufus. "Library's closed!" And off he went, whistling.

Rufus looked after him. The fellow said the library was closed. How could it have closed so fast? He had been here such a little while ago. The lady must still be here. He did want his Brownie book. If only he could see in, he might see the lady and get his book. The windows were high up but they had very wide sills. Rufus was a wonderful climber. He could shinny up trees and poles faster than anybody on the block. Faster than Joey. Now, helping himself up by means of one of the pine trees that grew close to the building, and by sticking his toes in the ivy and rough places in the bricks, he scrambled up the wall. He hoisted himself up on one of the sills and sat there. He peered in. It was dark inside, for the shades had been drawn almost all the way down.

"Library lady!" he called, and he knocked on the windowpane. There was no answer. He put his hands on each side of his face to shield his eyes, and he looked in for a long, long time. He could not believe that she had left. Rufus was resolved to get a book. He had lost track of the number of times he had been back and forth from home to the library, and the library home. Maybe the lady was in the cellar. He climbed down, stubbing his big toe on the bricks as he did so. He stooped down beside one of the low dirt-spattered cellar windows. He couldn't see in. He lay flat on the ground, wiped one spot clean on the window, picked up a few pieces of coal from the sill and put them in his pocket for Mama.

"Hey, lady," he called.

He gave the cellar window a little push. It wasn't locked so he opened it a little and looked in. All he could see was a high pile of coal reaching up to this window. Of course he didn't put any of that coal in his pocket for that would be stealing.

"Hey, lady!" he yelled again. His voice echoed in the cellar but the library lady did not answer. He called out, "Hey, lady," every few seconds, but all that answered him was an echo. He pushed the window open a little wider. All of a sudden it swung wide open and Rufus slid in, right on top of the coal pile, and crash, clatter, bang! He slid to the bottom, making a great racket.

A little light shone through the dusty windows, but on the whole it was very dark and spooky down here and Rufus really wished that he was back on the outside look-ing in. However, since he was in the library, why not go upstairs quick, get the Brownie book, and go home? The window had banged shut, but he thought he could climb up the coal pile, pull the window up, and get out. He certainly hoped he could any-way. Supposing he couldn't and he had to stay in this cellar! Well, that he would not think about. He looked around in the dusky light and saw a staircase across the cellar. Luckily his application was still good. It was torn and dirty but it still had his name on it, RUFUS M, and that was the impor-tant part. He'd leave this on the desk in exchange for the Brownie book.

Rufus cautiously made his way over to the steps but he stopped halfway across the cellar. Somebody had opened the door at the top of the stairs. He couldn't see who it was, but he did see the light reflected and that's how he knew that somebody had opened the door. It must be the lady. He was just going to say, "Hey, lady," when he thought, "Gee, maybe it isn't the lady. Maybe it's a spooky thing."

Then the light went away, the door was closed, and Rufus was left in the dark again. He didn't like it down here. He started to go back to the coal pile to get out of this place. Then he felt of his application. What a lot of work he had done to get a book and now that he was this near to getting one, should he give up? No. Anyway, if it was the lady up there, he knew her and she knew him and neither one of them was scared of the other. And Mama always said there's no such thing as a spooky thing.

So Rufus bravely made his way again to the stairs. He tiptoed up them. The door at the head was not closed tightly. He pushed it open and found himself right in the library. But goodness! There in the little sink room right opposite him was the library lady!

Rufus stared at her in silence. The library lady was eating. Rufus had never seen her do anything before but play cards, punch books, and carry great piles of them around. Now she was eating. Mama said not to stare at anybody while they were eating. Still Rufus didn't know the library lady ate, so it was hard for him not to look at her.

She had a little gas stove in there. She could cook there. She was reading a book at the same time that she was eating. Sylvie could do that too. This lady did not see him.

"Hey, lady," said Rufus.

The librarian jumped up out of her seat. "Was that you in the cellar? I thought I heard somebody. Goodness, young man! I thought you had gone home long ago."

Rufus didn't say anything. He just stood there. He had gone home and he had come back lots of times. He had the whole thing in his mind; the coming and going, and going and coming, and sliding down the coal pile, but he did not know where to begin, how to tell it.

"Didn't you know the library is closed now?" she demanded, coming across the floor with firm steps.

Rufus remained silent. No, he hadn't known it. The fellow had told him but he hadn't believed him. Now he could see for himself that the library was closed so the library lady could eat. If the lady would let him take his book, he'd go home and stay there. He'd play the game of Find the Duke with Jane. He hopefully held out his card with his name on it.

"Here this is," he said.

But the lady acted as though she didn't even see it. She led Rufus over to the door.

"All right now," she said. "Out with you!" But just as she opened the door the sound of water boiling over on the stove struck their ears, and back she raced to her little room.

"Gracious!" she exclaimed. "What a day!"

Before the door could close on him, Rufus followed her in and sat down on the edge of a chair. The lady thought he had gone and started to sip her tea. Rufus watched her quietly, waiting for her to finish.

After a while the lady brushed the crumbs off her lap. And then she washed her hands and the dishes in the little sink where Rufus had washed his hands. In a library a lady could eat and could wash. Maybe she slept here too. Maybe she lived here.

"Do you live here?" Rufus asked her.

"Mercy on us!" exclaimed the lady. "Where'd you come from? Didn't I send you home? No, I don't live here and neither do you. Come now, out with you, young man. I mean it." The lady called all boys "young man" and all girls "Susie." She came out of the little room and she opened the big brown door again. "There," she said. "Come back on Thursday."

Rufus's eyes filled up with tears.

"Here's this," he said again, holding up his application in a last desperate attempt. But the lady shook her head. Rufus went slowly down the steps, felt around in the bushes for his scooter, and with drooping spirits he mounted it. Then for the second time that day, the library lady changed her mind.

"Oh, well," she said, "come back here, young man. I'm not supposed to do business when the library's closed, but I see we'll have to make an exception."

So Rufus rubbed his sooty hands over his face, hid his scooter in the bushes again, climbed the granite steps and, without circling the light, he went back in and gave the lady his application.

The lady took it gingerly. "My, it's dirty," she said. "You really ought to sign another one."

"And go home with it?" asked Rufus. He really didn't believe this was possible. He wiped his hot face on his sleeve and looked up at the lady in exhaustion. What he was thinking was: All right. If he had to sign another one, all right. But would she just please stay open until he got back?

However, this was not necessary. The lady said, "Well now, I'll try to clean this old one up. But remember, young man, always have everything clean—your hands, your book, everything, when you come to the library."

Rufus nodded solemnly. "My feet too," he assured her.

Then the lady made Rufus wash his hands again. They really were very bad this time, for he had been in a coal pile, and now at last she gave Rufus the book he wanted—one of the Palmer Cox Brownie books. This one was "The Brownies in the Philippines."

And Rufus went home.

When he reached home, he showed Mama his book. She smiled at him, and gave his cheek a pat. She thought it was fine that he had gone to the library and joined all by himself and taken out a book. And she thought it was fine when Rufus sat down at the kitchen table, was busy and quiet for a long, long time, and then showed her what he had done.

He had printed RUFUS M. That was what he had done. And that's the way he learned to sign his name.

INTO THE LIGHT OF DAY

from CHILD OF THE SILENT NIGHT
by Edith Fisher Hunter
illustrated by James Watling

When she was two years old, Laura Bridgman became very ill with scarlet fever and was left blind and deaf. Her parents were afraid that she would never be able to communicate with the people around her or to learn about the world. However, Dr. Samuel Gridley Howe, the director of the Perkins Institution for the Blind in Boston, wanted to try to teach her. Dr. Howe intended to first teach Laura the twenty-six letters of the alphabet and then help her to understand that people could share their thoughts by combining these letters into words.

When the first lesson began Laura was seated at a table across from Dr. Howe. Beside her sat Miss Drew, who was to be Laura's own special teacher. Miss Jeannette Howe sat watching nearby.

The doctor had arranged a row of objects on the table in front of him. There were a large key, a spoon, a knife, a fork, a book, a cup and a few other things with which he felt sure Laura would be familiar.

First Dr. Howe put the key into Laura's hand. It was a very large key. He let her handle it and feel it all over. She knew immediately what it was. The key at home with which she locked her boot in the cupboard was very much like this one—except for one thing. Her sensitive fingers paused as they felt the long key. There was something *on* this one.

Dr. Howe had fastened a paper label on the key. On the label the word *key* was written in a special kind of raised

lettering or embossing that was used at that time in writing for the blind. The Braille system, now so widely used, had not yet been adopted. Dr. Howe guided Laura's fingers over the raised lines of the letters several times. She had no idea, of course, what the letters were.

Then he took the key away from Laura and handed her a spoon. She took it, felt it and immediately recognized it as a spoon much like the ones with which she set the table at home. Again there was one important difference. Along the handle of the spoon Dr. Howe had pasted a label with the letters S-P-O-O-N written in raised type. Dr. Howe guided her fingers carefully over this word several times.

Now the doctor took away the spoon and gave the key back to Laura. He directed her fingers to the label on the key again. Then he gave her back the spoon and directed her fingers to the label on the spoon once more. He wanted Laura to feel that the shape of the lines on the key label and the shape of the lines on the spoon label were just as different from each other as the key and spoon themselves were different from one another.

Now the doctor did something else. He took away the key and the spoon and gave Laura just a piece of paper with some raised letters on it. The letters were K-E-Y again. Taking the key once more, Dr. Howe directed Laura's fingers to the label on it.

An expression on Laura's face made it quite clear that she recognized that the raised letters were the same on both papers, the one on the key and the separate label. Dr. Howe went through the same process with the spoon and a separate label that read S-P-O-O-N.

The rest of that first lesson was spent letting Laura feel the remaining objects—cup, knife, book, and so forth—and the labels for these, both those pasted on the object and those that were separate. From that time on Laura had lessons every morning and afternoon. She seemed to enjoy them thoroughly and to consider them just a game, not work. It was difficult for Dr. Howe and Miss Drew to get her to stop "playing" this game.

By about the third day Dr. Howe and Miss Drew were delighted to see that Laura had grasped the important point that the separate label for *key* somehow went with the key and the label that was separate from the spoon went with the spoon. That she understood this was shown by the fact that

she could take a separate label, such as the one spelling *book*, and feel about until she found a book without any label. Then she would place the label on the book.

In a very few days Laura could reverse this process. She could pick up an object, such as a spoon, search through a pile of loose labels on the table, feel them until she found the one that read S-P-O-O-N and then put it on a spoon. She could do this for any object for which she had been taught the feeling of the word.

Dr. Howe was greatly encouraged. He felt sure that he was going to succeed with Laura; his only question was how long it was going to take him. In a report that he once wrote about his work with her he said: "It sometimes occurred to me that she was like a person alone and helpless in a deep, dark, still pit, and that I was letting down a cord and dangling it about, in hopes she might find it, and that finally she would seize it by chance, and clinging to it, be drawn up by it into the light of day and into human society."

The lessons were going so well that Dr. Howe felt Laura was ready to take another important step forward. He had Miss Drew cut the labels for the words *key, spoon, knife*, and so forth, into separate letters. Up until this time Laura had seen words as wholes. Now he wanted her to learn that they are made up of parts—letters. Laura was allowed to follow closely, with her hands, all that Miss Drew did. After the words had been cut into separate letters, her hands followed Miss Drew's as she arranged the letters back into words.

In an astonishingly short time Laura had grasped the point of this new "game." If Miss Drew handed her the letters O, S,

N, O, P, in a flash Laura could arrange them in the correct order to spell S-P-O-O-N. If Miss Drew gave her Y, K, E, Laura arranged them into the word K-E-Y. O, K, O, B and I, K, E, N, F were equally simple for her. After a few more lessons Laura could do this with all the words in her vocabulary and soon after that she could take from a whole pile of loose letters whatever ones she wanted and spell correctly any word she wished of those she had been taught.

Dr. Howe thought it would be easier for Laura to arrange the letters if there were some kind of form into which they could be fitted. Therefore he had metal letters—types, he called them—made for her and a frame with grooves into which the letters could be fitted. He had four complete sets made of the twenty-six letters of the alphabet. Within a short time Laura was using the metal letters to build all the words she knew.

Two months had passed before Dr. Howe felt that Laura was ready to take the final step that he had planned for her. Miss Drew was sent to the home of a Mr. George Loring, who was deaf, to learn the manual alphabet. She learned it in one afternoon.

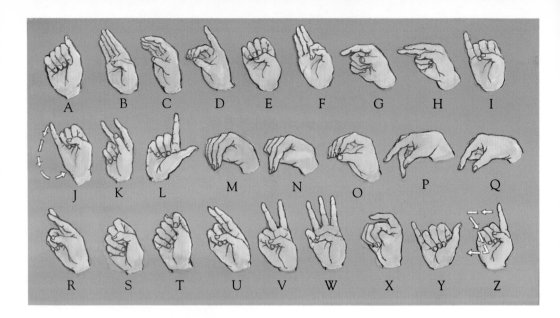

The manual alphabet is a way of forming the twenty-six letters of the alphabet with the hands. In the United States the one-handed manual alphabet is used. There is also a two-handed system used in some countries. In the one-handed system the letter *a*, for example, is formed by folding the four fingers over and keeping the thumb straight. *B* is formed by holding the fingers straight up with the thumb folded in. In only a few cases, as with *c* and *y*, for example, does the hand form a shape that very much resembles the shape of that letter as we write it.

A deaf person who has been "talking" with the manual alphabet for a long time can "say" with his hand as many as 130 words a minute. A deaf person who is skilled at watching another person "speak" with his hands can easily "read" 130 words a minute.

Laura, of course, would not be able to see the letters. Miss Drew would have to form them in Laura's hand so that she could feel them.

But how could she teach Laura that the various positions in which she held her fingers meant the letters of the alphabet that she had already learned with raised letters and metal types? This is how Miss Drew did it. She picked up the key and let Laura feel it. Then she took the letter K from the set of metal types and let Laura feel that. Then she shaped the letter *k* in the manual alphabet into Laura's hand, her first two fingers up and bent forward, the next two fingers folded down, and the thumb up. She made Laura feel the way her fingers were held. Then she let Laura feel the metal letter K again.

The same procedure was followed with the letter *e*. First Laura must feel the metal type of the E, then Miss Drew formed *e* in the manual alphabet, all the fingers folded over and the thumb folded down, and then back to the metal type again. Finally the letter Y was taken from the metal types and Laura allowed to feel it. The manual *y* is formed with thumb up, little finger up and other fingers all folded down. This one almost looks like a *y* as we write it. Now Miss Drew had set the metal types K-E-Y in the form.

She let Laura run her hand over the whole word. Then she formed again, in the manual alphabet, the letters *k-e-y* in Laura's hand and she placed the key itself in Laura's other hand. This was done with the spoon, the cup, and the key again.

And then it happened! For two months Laura had been "playing" these games with letters and words almost the way a trained dog performs certain tricks. Now, suddenly, it was different. Dr. Howe always said that he knew almost the exact moment when Laura's face showed that she at last really understood what all this meant. Suddenly it seemed to become clear to her that every object had a name, that these names could be spelled by letters, either in raised letters, metal types or, most easily of all, by the manual alphabet.

In one of his yearly reports about his work with Laura Bridgman, Dr. Howe wrote: ". . . Now the truth began to flash upon her, her intellect began to work, she perceived that here was a way by which she could herself make up a sign of anything that was in her own mind, and show it to another mind, and at once her countenance lighted up with a human expression . . . I could almost fix upon the moment when this truth dawned upon her mind and spread its light to her countenance. . . ."

Laura had found the rope that Dr. Howe was dangling before her. She had caught hold of it at last and could be drawn up from the dark pit in which she lived into the light of day!

What a different world it was for Laura now!

Can you imagine what it must have been like for her? She had been alive for eight years and yet until this day she had never been able really to ask a single question! Now, suddenly, she could ask at least one enormous question: WHAT IS THE NAME OF THAT?

Of course she didn't know the words *what, is, the, name, of,* and *that,* but now by placing her hand on any object, she let her teacher know that she was asking for the name of that object.

And ask she did! At supper on the day she really understood that every object has a name, poor Miss Drew didn't get a bite to eat. Laura wanted the name of everything and everybody. Usually at meals Miss Drew was expected to help not only Laura but several of the little blind girls. She cut their meat, buttered their bread and did anything else that needed doing. But tonight Laura demanded every single bit of Miss Drew's attention.

"I'll help with the other children," said Miss Jeannette. "This one meal we'll let Laura have you wholly to herself. It's a kind of birthday for her."

And so Laura began. She placed her hand on her napkin, and Miss Drew spelled "napkin" into Laura's hand. Then Laura spelled it into Miss Drew's hand. Then she asked the name of the tablecloth, the salt, the pepper, the sugar, the milk, and on and on and on. Miss Drew was thoroughly exhausted when she went to bed that night and the muscles of her spelling hand ached for hours.

MUKASA AT SCHOOL

from MUKASA by John Nagenda
illustrated by Tyrone Geter

Mukasa lives in a small village in Uganda in the 1940s and is the first of his family to go to school. Until his mother found a way to pay for his school fees and his uniform, Mukasa had assumed he would spend his life herding goats. Because reading and writing are almost unknown in his village, school has a special wonder for ten-year-old Mukasa.

Mukasa's teacher, Miss Nanteza, said, "How many of you know anything about reading and writing? Put up your hands."

Mukasa saw to his surprise that one of the boys put his hand up. He was the only one. Mukasa had not thought it was possible to learn these things before you came to school. The boy had a rather pleased look on his face which Mukasa found annoying. He also noticed that the boy's uniform looked smarter than his own.

Miss Nanteza said, "All right, Kalanzi. Anybody else?"

Later Mukasa found out that Kalanzi was Miss Nanteza's second cousin. Kalanzi's parents were the richest people for miles around, and in fact they had had Miss Nanteza give him lessons before he started school.

Miss Nanteza said, "If you all pay attention, most of you won't find it very difficult to follow what I am going to teach you."

Slates were passed around, together with funny-looking sticklike objects which left a mark when you scratched the slates with them.

Miss Nanteza started with the alphabet. She wrote a letter on the blackboard and said it out loud. The class said it after her and scratched its likeness on their slates. Then after about five letters, Miss Nanteza had everything wiped off. When that was done she wrote the letters down again and asked what each was.

Up went Kalanzi's hand immediately. After the second time she told him that until the rest of the class had caught up with him, she would not call on him to answer. The whole class laughed loudly at this, but Mukasa, although he too

laughed, felt a little sorry for Kalanzi; after all, it wasn't his fault that he already knew the answer.

As for himself, he was having a wonderful time. He had often wondered whether he would find it difficult to learn. At home if he was told something he always remembered it, indeed on some occasions he had annoyed his parents by remembering things which they would have preferred forgotten. But he had thought that school learning might be different. Now he discovered that once the teacher had written a letter and said it out loud, and once he had written it down himself, it seemed to stick in his mind. And what's more it seemed to make sense in itself so that the way it looked gave it a character of its own.

Before coming to school, Mukasa had from time to time seen old pieces of paper with writing on them; for example the shopkeeper sometimes used them for packaging. But every time Mukasa had looked closely at the writing, all he could think of were swarming little insects. Now it was as if Miss Nanteza gave sound and meaning to them.

Miss Nanteza filled the blackboard with more and more letters and then a few words, and it seemed to Mukasa as if a treasure chest were being opened up and offered to him. As if by magic, what had been an empty space on the wall was now covered, right before him, by all manner of exciting and mysterious things. If this was what learning was about, he was going to love it.

When Miss Nanteza rubbed the letters off, the dust of the chalk drifted over the whole class and to Mukasa even the somewhat biting sensation he felt in his nose was full of excitement.

He wished Miss Nanteza would move more quickly. By now he had almost forgotten about the others in the class. It was as if everything the teacher said was for him alone.

Every time Miss Nanteza asked a question, almost before she had completed it, Mukasa's hand shot up. But after a time he noticed that she would leave his hand up and look straight past him, and ask the question of someone who didn't even understand it, and in the meantime his own upraised arm would be getting unbearably heavy. He heard one or two sniggers from some of the class whenever this happened. On one occasion he caught Kalanzi openly laughing at him. Then finally just before the end of the day, when Mukasa stood up to answer yet another question, someone hit him on the back of the head with a piece of chalk.

"Who did that?" shouted the teacher.

Nobody answered. Mukasa had looked around quickly and he had seen who had thrown the chalk. Usually he wouldn't have told, but by now he was so fed up that before he knew it he had blurted out, "It was that nasty boy over there in the back row!"

"Come here, Mutahi," Miss Nanteza ordered.

The boy came forward slowly. Miss Nanteza reached out and like lightning slapped him twice, on either side of his face. The look Mutahi gave Mukasa as he walked back to his seat was ferocious.

After school Mukasa was walking past the staff room when he heard his teacher's voice. Something made him stop and listen.

He could hardly believe his ears: ". . . a real firecracker; his name is Mukasa, probably too good for his class!"

Mukasa was still floating on air from that remark when he turned a corner. Mutahi was waiting.

It was only a brief fight before someone separated them, but it was long enough for Mukasa to know that he would have had no chance of winning it.

It didn't matter. There wasn't a thing on this wonderful evening that could for long detract from his happiness and he was almost singing as he ran home to tell his family all about it.

After the second day of classes he could write his name. When he had written it he looked at it for a long time and it seemed to be his name even more than ever before, and he thought it even looked like him.

He walked home with his name tucked away inside his exercise book.

"Look, look," he said, trying to appear calm and collected. "That's my name and I wrote it myself; with my own hand!"

He passed the book around.

"Now is not that something?" his mother exclaimed. She was looking at the writing as if she half expected it to come to life and shake her by the hand.

His grandparents were looking at it upside down.

It was while Mukasa was explaining how it all added up that his father came home.

"That's Mu and that's Ka and that's Sa. Mukasa," Mukasa said.

MEET JOHN NAGENDA, AUTHOR

Nagenda was born in Uganda in 1938, and Mukasa *describes the way of life he knew there as a child. Nagenda explains:*
"This story is set in the Uganda of the early 1940s. It takes place in a small village where most of the people are very poor in the money sense; they find it much more difficult to buy things, including education, than their fellows in towns or villages nearer to bigger towns. And of course they are far more tied to a traditional way of life.

"If you went to Mukasa's village today you would notice changes. For a start, the outside world has made more of an impact upon it. This is the result of better communications, and also because so many of the villagers have been to the towns, mainly to search for work. And of those who never left the village, quite a few possess radio sets and therefore know about other parts of the country and beyond.

"As for going to school, the chances are much better today, and in Mukasa's village there are fewer children who would now look forward only to a life of tending goats. But it is still true that many who go to school even today might go for just a couple of years before they are overtaken by lack of fees or classroom space.

"Perhaps the differences are not really as great as they seem, and it is truer to say that it is the tempo and flavor of village life that have changed. The steady rhythm of the village background has been drastically upset. At the same time the villagers lack the means of creating a worthwhile substitute. In other words, today Mukasa would find it easier to go to school, but unless he were very lucky, the horizons which schooling opened to him would remain as far off and elusive as ever."

DO BANANAS CHEW GUM?

from the book by Jamie Gilson
illustrated by Beth Roberge

*Although Sam Mott is in sixth grade, he can barely
read or write. His mother worries about his future. His father
tries to help Sam by reading Sam's schoolbooks aloud to him
each night and by doing most of Sam's homework. Now in a
new town and a new school, Sam hides his disability by playing
the part of the class clown. Eventually his classmates and his
teacher catch on. In a class spelling bee, Sam is unable to spell
the word "cute." Sam's teacher then arranges for him to take a
series of tests with the school's learning disabilities specialist,
Ms. Huggins.*

I trudged down to room 102. It looked like a closet from the outside, mostly because it didn't have a window like the rest of the doors did. I knocked. Very lightly, so whoever was inside wouldn't hear.

"Come in. Come in," a voice called out.

I opened the door slowly and saw that it was a little room, not closet-sized, but little, painted green like the garbage room. There was a desk, a few chairs, and a crescent-shaped table, yellow-green like a slice of honeydew melon. The lady inside said hello. She was standing up and she was almost as tall as my dad. Her face was round and shiny and she had lots of curly dark hair.

"I know you," I told her, and without even checking my dragon ring, I stuck out my hand. She shook it with both of hers.

"My name is Ms. Huggins," she said.

I did know her. She was always stopping in our room and talking to kids or to Mrs. Bird. I didn't know she was the learning disabilities person, though. That really knocked me

out. I mean, she was at school *all* the time. That had to mean there were a *lot* of dumb kids like me. She let me sit down at the crescent table.

"Well, Sammy," she said, smiling, like she was tickled to death I'd decided to come.

"My name is Sam," I told her. Somehow I didn't want Ms. Huggins calling me the wrong name.

"OK, Sam," she said. "We've a job to do. I'm going to give you some tests today and again next Monday to find out how you learn best."

"That's what my dad said." I shrugged and stared down at the green floor. Green tile. It was very dull. "I don't know what else you need to know," I said, like I couldn't care less. I mean, she was nice and I really didn't want her to find out more about me.

"I expect you know more about yourself than anybody else," she said. "We can start there." She sat down in a chair across from me. "What do you do best, Sam?"

"Me?" I looked up. What a stupid question, I thought. Do *best?* "I don't know. Make people laugh at me, I guess. I'm good at that."

"You mean jokes? Like 'Why did the robber take a shower at the bank?' "

"Because he wanted to make a clean getaway," I flipped back. "No, mostly not jokes. Mostly *at* me." I shrugged again, like, of course, I didn't care.

"Come on, Sam. Mrs. Bird tells me you have a special ability in math. She says you're a bright boy."

"I light up the night."

"Ah, you're a sit-down comic. Then they *do* laugh because you want them to, sometimes. How about the math?"

"I know a few tricks with numbers, that's all. I'm mostly dumb."

She laughed. Laughed. I could have punched her. She wasn't so nice after all. "No, it can't be that easy," she went on, still looking much too cheerful. "You're not allowed in my door unless you're smart. Children with a low ability level don't come to me. There's another teacher who works with them."

She'd change her mind soon enough. I wasn't going to argue with her. I'd just let her start the tests. That'd show her. I stared out the window while she got some books and paper out, wondering just *how* smart people were different from me. I tried to imagine what was in their heads that wasn't in mine.

"I'm going to ask you some crazy questions, Sam," she said.

I looked up at her, wondering what she could ask that was crazy, and why.

"First," she said, "do bananas chew gum?"

I laughed out loud. "Are you kidding?"

"Not at all," she said. "Do clocks swim?"

"No, but time flies." Mom was always big on riddles. Were these riddles that I wasn't smart enough to figure out?

"Do babies cry?"

That wasn't a trick. "Sometimes."

But then they started getting harder. After a while it was stuff like "Do interpreters translate?" Pretty soon the only word that made sense was "Do." I had to keep saying, "I don't know," and feeling like an idiot. But just when they were getting so hard I bet *she* didn't even know the answers, we started on something completely different.

Lots of pictures. You had to match them. Like this one I remember that had a baseball on one side of the page and on the other side pictures of a violin bow, a rake, and a baseball bat. Really simp stuff. But they got harder, too.

Pretty much every new part started out easy and got hard like that. There were lots of different kinds of things, like when Ms. Huggins laid these tiles down on a table and all the tiles had weird lines on them and squiggles and she'd say, "Which shape is different from the rest?" or she'd put up

another and say, "Find this shape. It's hidden in that picture." She was timing all this stuff with a stopwatch, and it was hard.

Then I was supposed to copy circles and arrows and boxes and stars and, boy, did I stink at that. So when we finally got to some math, it was like a vacation, or at least recess. It was real 2 plus 2 stuff to begin with. Then it got to be $5\frac{1}{3}$ times $2\frac{1}{5}$ equals, and then long division with decimals. She only gave me ten minutes to get it all done, but before the time was nearly up I got to these questions I didn't even know what they meant.

"That's OK," she said, "you won't learn how to do those problems until seventh grade. I knew we'd get to something you do really well. You were terrific at the math. Fast, accurate, all those good things. I doubt there's anyone in your class who could do so well."

"Alicia," I told her.

"Don't know her."

"You wouldn't."

"She pretty good at math?"

"She's good at everything. A brain." My stomach felt like lunchtime was getting close. I didn't want to start any more tests. I decided to stall. "Why is it easy for me to do math and not reading?" I asked her, even though I knew the answer. (*Dum-dum-dum.*)

She shook her head. "I'm not sure. Nobody's sure. Did you know some people can hardly do math at all? Some people just blink their eyes and shake their heads when you say that 4 plus 15 is 19. It's as if they've got a short circuit in their heads and they can't put numbers through their brain computer. If they're smart otherwise, that's a learning disability, too."

"Can they read?"

"Sometimes. Sometimes not. Learning disabilities come in all varieties."

"Like ice cream."

"More even than that." She smiled, like she knew I was stalling. "Ready for another test?"

"No," I said. "Is it hard?"

"I think so. Yes. This one's spelling."

"Yuck. Isn't it time for lunch?"

She checked her watch. "Eleven-ten. Not quite. Just this last one, OK? Then we'll break for lunch."

But geez, it was awful. After "dog" and "cat" and "hat" to make me feel like it wasn't going to be all that bad, it was word after word after word I couldn't spell and I knew I was guessing wrong. At least she didn't ask me to spell "cute."

"Try sounding it out," she'd say. "Try it out loud. Keep plugging." But how do you keep plugging on "similar" and "license" and "miracle" when you hardly know how to begin? I didn't care if I *ever* knew how to spell them. I mean, who cares, anyway? Every word more I sank lower and lower in the chair. My stomach growled like a mad dog.

After I guess she figured she'd tortured me enough, Ms. Huggins beamed out this huge smile even though I knew there wasn't anything to grin about. "Cheer up," she said. "It's chow time."

I didn't smile back.

"You're doing fine. I'm finding out a lot about how you can learn even better. And the math was fabulous."

"That's me, fabulous Sam." What a fake she is, I decided. Always smiling and saying "terrific" when what she means is dumb. I get mad at Mom but at least she knows dumb when she sees it and doesn't lie about it.

"Do I have to come back?"

"Around one-thirty," she said, "we'll start afresh. Why don't you go early to the cafeteria and take a long lunch hour. I'll give you a note. I think I hear a hungry monster in your stomach."

It wasn't funny, so I didn't pretend it was. I just stared at her.

While she wrote out the pink permission slip I got up and hung around the door.

"See you at one-thirty," she said, holding out the paper. "Right after the party."

I started to bolt out the door. "Party?"

"Didn't Mrs. Bird say there'd be a party after lunch?"

"Oh, yeah," I said, remembering. "There'll be a bunch of bananas hanging around up there chewing gum and eating cupcakes." And I slammed the door on her silly smile.

The lunch hour went on forever. We had pizza casserole. Not many kids like it so an awful lot got smashed up in the trash compacter. I threw away about half of mine, even though I'll eat almost anything.

After lunch I sat by myself, watched the first graders play, and then poked around in the grass with a stick, pretending to dig up treasures. All I found was a rusty nail and a few ants, who crawled all over a cookie crumb I fed them.

When the bell rang there wasn't anything to do but go back inside with the big stream of kids, like I was a fish on a hook. And there wasn't anything inside I wanted to do.

Mrs. Bird's room was all laughs and giggles. It sounded so happy when I slammed my locker door I wondered if maybe it wouldn't be a great party after all. I was the last kid in, but Mrs. Bird hadn't gotten back from her lunch yet.

"Cutie," a girl yelled. "Did you see your cupcake yet?" I looked around the room, and on every desk was a cupcake, a napkin, and a paper cup with something in it. But kids were gathered around my desk like the ants on the crumb.

"Mine has AB on it for the birthday girl. What does it say on yours, Cutes?" a boy asked with a smirk.

"How do you *spell* it?" somebody giggled. They were really starting to laugh at me.

And I got mad. I got so mad I could have zapped them. I *know* getting mad makes it worse, but I could feel my face get red and I felt like I could level them all. I straight-armed the guy nearest me. Alicia just stood there by her desk and looked confused. It was like she knew she kept botching me up and didn't understand how.

The stupid cupcake sat there. SAM was on it with a red heart iced around the letters. I hadn't even noticed *that* before.

"What does it *say?*" somebody in the back asked. "Does it really say 'cute'?"

I picked up the cupcake and held it up high for them to see. I shouted so everyone could hear, "It says Sam. That's my name. I don't want to be called anything else. And don't you forget it." They looked at me with their mouths open and I stared them down, feeling tall like a statue.

I would have kept talking, too, but Mrs. Bird came back. She stood at the door of the silent room, trying to decide what was going on. Her eyes fixed on me.

"Sammy," she called out. I didn't move. I just got madder. "Sammy," she went on, "were you screaming? I could hear you down the hall."

"I was saying," I told her in less than a shout, "that my name is Sam. And I don't want to be called Sammy or New Kid or Metal Mouth or Dumbhead or—especially—Cutes. I don't want to be called anything but Sam Mott."

"That sounds reasonable to me," she said mildly. "Everybody agree to that?"

There was a kind of general mumbling and I sat down in my seat, feeling like a balloon somebody had let the air out of— like I had been all filled up with being mad and now it was gone I just felt bad. Mrs. Bird just didn't understand. I ate the top off the cupcake. The room was still very quiet.

"That was really something," Wally whispered.

I nodded, my mouth full of sweet stuff. Gulping it down, I said, "I was mad."

"Yeah," he said, "I could tell."

We all had to sing "Happy Birthday" to Alicia. And I sang it like almost everybody else did, "Happy birthday to you, you belong in a zoo. You look like a monkey, and you smell like one, too." I mean, that's the way we *always* sang it. There'd been about four birthdays since I'd been in this school and mostly everybody sang it that way. It wasn't being mean to Alicia, like name calling. After my big speech it worried me some. But I don't think it was. She didn't look mad.

After we finished eating the cupcakes and drinking lemonade, the Bird gave all the captains math problems to pass back. Then she stopped at my desk and leaned over. "Are you all right?" she asked and I nodded. "You may be excused, Sam," she said. "I would have called you Sam sooner if I'd known."

"Oh, it wasn't just you," I told her, and hurried out of the room while almost everybody else was groaning over the math.

I knocked on the door of room 102.

"Come in. Come in," Ms. Huggins called like before. When I opened it, she said, "You're back!" like she was surprised but glad. "How's the monster in your stomach?"

"Just fed him a cupcake and he's happy," I told her. I didn't know why I wasn't mad at her anymore.

We started out with easy stuff. Numbers.

"Repeat after me," she said, "17-1-4-42." Stuff like that. And it wasn't hard at all. A piece of cake. A piece of *cup*cake.

"Do you see?" she asked me when the test was over. "Do you see how much easier it is for you to learn from what you *hear* than from what you read? You remembered those so well."

The test had seemed easy. I did see, sort of.

"You don't have to read things to learn them," she went on. "Most people learn a lot by listening to other people, to movies, to television. You can even learn to *read* better by listening to *yourself*."

That sounded crazy. "How?"

"Just say there's a word you want to read . . ." she started.

"There *is*," I told her. "There is!" I'd stuck the archeology book Brenda had left for me in the orange crate with my good junk. I'd looked through it and even read a little bit of it. But I still couldn't figure out the word on the cover. I was sure it must be "archeology."

"Archeology," I said, almost begging. "That's the word I want to read. Can you teach me that one?"

"Good grief, you start at the top, don't you?" She wrote the word down for me on a piece of white paper, kind of splitting it up into parts—ARC-HE-OL-O-GY. "It isn't the easiest word to sound out, but . . ."

Then she took another piece of paper and tore a little square hole out of the middle. She put the hole on the word so I could just see the first three letters and she made me sound it out. Twice. And I did it. She moved the paper and I sounded out all the parts. Then she had me do that about ten times before she let me look at the word whole. And I could sound it out. Arc-he-ol-o-gy. Archeology. I kept looking at the word and saying it over. Out loud. Archeology. I was so excited I felt dizzy.

"Can I have the paper with the hole?"

"My compliments. But it's not magic. You've got to do the work."

Then I looked at the paper and wondered how many words in the new book I could do that way by myself. But she kept after me. "Sam, that was terrific! The computer in your head sometimes gets confused by a lot of letters. If you just let it see a few at a time for a while, it'll help.

"There are so many things you can do, Sam. Have somebody record the pages you have to read, then listen to the tape as you read the words to yourself. Then try making a tape of your voice reading the words. Can you do that?"

"No kidding?" I asked her. "A tape recorder? It would be OK? My mom said it would be a crutch."

"Nothing's wrong with a crutch if you need one. If you had a broken leg she'd let you have a crutch. If you've got a tape recorder, put it on your desk to take notes for you. I'll talk to Mrs. Bird about it. Reporters take notes with tape recorders all the time."

"I'm earning the money for one right now!" I'd tell Mrs. Glass and she'd let me keep on baby-sitting. I was sure she would.

Then we started another test and I had to guess which of a list of words fit best into paragraphs that were hard to read and I felt awful again.

"This would be easy for Alicia and Wally," I told Ms. Huggins. "It's not fair."

"Right," she said, "it's not. Wouldn't be fair if you fell off your bike and broke your elbow either, but you'd have to deal with it, fair or not. You can either give up and just plug your head into a TV set or you can work like crazy. I can help. Your folks can help. A lot of people can help. But in the end it's got to be you."

Then she gave me another test. There was this one word at the top and five words listed under it. I was supposed to find the word that meant nearly the same as the word at the top. Like there'd be "nap" and under it would be "jump," "roll," "bad," and "sleep." Ms. Huggins said if I couldn't decide which word fit best to just go on to the next question. After the first four or five I was a disaster.

"You'll get there, Sam," she said when I started sagging down in my chair.

"Never," I groaned.

"Listen," she told me, still cheerful like I was winning the race, not crawling along on my knees, "Thomas Edison had a learning disability in school, and so did Hans Christian Andersen, and Vice President Rockefeller, and President Wilson. They didn't get famous by saying 'never.' They worked their way out of it. You can, too, but you have to do it a step at a time. Nobody's going to wave a wand."

When I left room 102 I felt better. Some. "We'll find out more about you next Monday, Sam Mott," she said. "After that we'll work together several times a week." It was like I'd just waded up to my ankles in cold Lake Michigan water knowing I had to swim across the lake and back again.

SEVENTH GRADE

Gary Soto
illustrated by Andy San Diego

On the first day of school, Victor stood in line half an hour before he came to a wobbly card table. He was handed a packet of papers and a computer card on which he listed his one elective, French. He already spoke Spanish and English, but he thought some day he might travel to France, where it was cool; not like Fresno, where summer days reached 110 degrees in the shade. There were rivers in France, and huge churches, and fair-skinned people everywhere, the way there were brown people all around Victor.

Besides, Teresa, a girl he had liked since they were in catechism classes at Saint Theresa's, was taking French, too. With any luck they would be in the same class. Teresa is going to be my girl this year, he promised himself as he left the gym full of students in their new fall clothes. She was cute. And good at math, too, Victor thought as he walked down the hall to his homeroom. He ran into his friend, Michael Torres, by the water fountain that never turned off.

They shook hands, *raza*-style, and jerked their heads at one another in a *saludo de vato*. "How come you're making a face?" asked Victor.

"I ain't making a face, *ese*. This *is* my face." Michael said his face had changed during the summer. He had read a GQ magazine that his older brother borrowed from the Book Mobile

and noticed that the male models all had the same look on their faces. They would stand, one arm around a beautiful woman, and *scowl*. They would sit at a pool, their rippled stomachs dark with shadow, and *scowl*. They would sit at dinner tables, cool drinks in their hands, and *scowl*.

"I think it works," Michael said. He scowled and let his upper lip quiver. His teeth showed along with the ferocity of his soul. "Belinda Reyes walked by a while ago and looked at me," he said.

Victor didn't say anything, though he thought his friend looked pretty strange. They talked about recent movies, baseball, their parents, and the horrors of picking grapes in order to buy their fall clothes. Picking grapes was like living in Siberia, except hot and more boring.

"What classes are you taking?" Michael said, scowling.

"French. How 'bout you?"

"Spanish. I ain't so good at it, even if I'm Mexican."

"I'm not either, but I'm better at it than math, that's for sure."

A tinny, three-beat bell propelled students to their homerooms. The two friends socked each other in the arm and went their ways, Victor thinking, man, that's weird. Michael thinks making a face makes him handsome.

On the way to his homeroom, Victor tried a scowl. He felt foolish, until out of the corner of his eye he saw a girl looking at him. Umm, he thought, maybe it does work. He scowled with greater conviction.

In homeroom, roll was taken, emergency cards were passed out, and they were given a bulletin to take home to their parents. The principal, Mr. Belton, spoke over the crackling loudspeaker, welcoming the students to a new year, new experiences, and new friendships. The students squirmed in their chairs and ignored him. They were anxious to go to first period. Victor sat calmly, thinking of Teresa, who sat two rows away, reading a paperback novel. This would be his lucky year. She was in his homeroom, and would probably be in his English and math classes. And, of course, French.

The bell rang for first period, and the students herded noisily through the door. Only Teresa lingered, talking with the homeroom teacher.

"So you think I should talk to Mrs. Gaines?" she asked the teacher. "She would know about ballet?"

"She would be a good bet," the teacher said. Then added, "Or the gym teacher, Mrs. Garza."

Victor lingered, keeping his head down and staring at his desk. He wanted to leave when she did so he could bump into her and say something clever.

He watched her on the sly. As she turned to leave, he stood up and hurried to the door, where he managed to catch her eye. She smiled and said, "Hi, Victor."

He smiled back and said, "Yeah, that's me." His brown face blushed. Why hadn't he said, "Hi, Teresa," or "How was your summer?" or something nice?

As Teresa walked down the hall, Victor walked the other way, looking back, admiring how gracefully she walked, one foot in front of the other. So much for being in the same class, he thought. As he trudged to English, he practiced scowling.

In English they reviewed the parts of speech. Mr. Lucas, a portly man, waddled down the aisle, asking, "What is a noun?"

"A person, place, or thing," said the class in unison.

"Yes, now somebody give me an example of a person—you, Victor Rodriguez."

"Teresa," Victor said automatically. Some of the girls giggled. They knew he had a crush on Teresa. He felt himself blushing again.

"Correct," Mr. Lucas said. "Now provide me with a place."

Mr. Lucas called on a freckled kid who answered, "Teresa's house with a kitchen full of big brothers."

After English, Victor had math, his weakest subject. He sat in the back by the window, hoping that he would not be called on. Victor understood most of the problems, but some of the stuff looked like the teacher made it up as she went along. It was confusing, like the inside of a watch.

After math he had a fifteen-minute break, then social studies, and, finally, lunch. He bought a tuna casserole with buttered rolls, some fruit cocktail, and milk. He sat with Michael, who practiced scowling between bites.

Girls walked by and looked at him.

"See what I mean, Vic?" Michael scowled. "They love it."

"Yeah, I guess so."

They ate slowly, Victor scanning the horizon for a glimpse of Teresa. He didn't see her. She must have brought lunch, he thought, and is eating outside. Victor scraped his plate and left Michael, who was busy scowling at a girl two tables away.

The small, triangle-shaped campus bustled with students talking about their new classes. Everyone was in a sunny mood. Victor hurried to the bag lunch area, where he sat down and opened his math book. He moved his lips as if he were reading, but his mind was somewhere else. He raised his eyes slowly and looked around. No Teresa.

He lowered his eyes, pretending to study, then looked slowly to the left. No Teresa. He turned a page in the book and stared at some math problems that scared him because he knew he would have to do them eventually. He looked to the right. Still no sign of her. He stretched out lazily in an attempt to disguise his snooping.

Then he saw her. She was sitting with a girlfriend under a plum tree. Victor moved to a table near her and daydreamed about taking her to a movie. When the bell sounded, Teresa looked up, and their eyes met. She smiled sweetly and gathered her books. Her next class was French, same as Victor's.

They were among the last students to arrive in class, so all the good desks in the back had already been taken. Victor was forced to sit near the front, a few desks away from Teresa, while Mr. Bueller wrote French words on the chalkboard. The bell rang, and Mr. Bueller wiped his hands, turned to the class, and said, *"Bonjour."*

"Bonjour," braved a few students.

"Bonjour," Victor whispered. He wondered if Teresa heard him.

Mr. Bueller said that if the students studied hard, at the end of the year they could go to France and be understood by the populace.

One kid raised his hand and asked, "What's 'populace'?"

"The people, the people of France."

Mr. Bueller asked if anyone knew French. Victor raised his hand, wanting to impress Teresa. The teacher beamed and said, *"Trés bien. Parlez-vous français?"*

Victor didn't know what to say. The teacher wet his lips and asked something else in French. The room grew silent. Victor felt all eyes staring at him. He tried to bluff his way out by making noises that sounded French.

"La me vava me con le grandma," he said uncertainly.

Mr. Bueller, wrinkling his face in curiosity, asked him to speak up.

Great rosebushes of red bloomed on Victor's cheeks. A river of nervous sweat ran down his palms. He felt awful. Teresa sat a few desks away, no doubt thinking he was a fool. Without looking at Mr. Bueller, Victor mumbled, "Frenchie oh wewe gee in September."

Mr. Bueller asked Victor to repeat what he had said.

"Frenchie oh wewe gee in September," Victor repeated.

Mr. Bueller understood that the boy didn't know French and turned away. He walked to the blackboard and pointed to the words on the board with his steel-edged ruler.

"Le bateau," he sang.

"Le bateau," the students repeated.

"Le bateau est sur l'eau," he sang.

"Le bateau est sur l'eau."

Victor was too weak from failure to join the class. He stared at the board and wished he had taken Spanish, not French. Better yet, he wished he could start his life over. He had never been so embarrassed. He bit his thumb until he tore off a sliver of skin.

The bell sounded for fifth period, and Victor shot out of the room, avoiding the stares of the other kids, but had to return for his math book. He looked sheepishly at the teacher, who was erasing the board, then widened his eyes in terror at Teresa who stood in front of him. "I didn't know you knew French," she said. "That was good."

Mr. Bueller looked at Victor, and Victor looked back. Oh please, don't say anything, Victor pleaded with his eyes. I'll wash your car, mow your lawn, walk your dog—anything! I'll be your best student, and I'll clean your erasers after school.

Mr. Bueller shuffled through the papers on his desk. He smiled and hummed as he sat down to work. He remembered his college years when he dated a girlfriend in borrowed cars. She thought he was rich because each time he picked her up he had a different car. It was fun until he had spent all his money on her and had to write home to his parents because he was broke.

Victor couldn't stand to look at Teresa. He was sweaty with shame. "Yeah, well, I picked up a few things from movies and books and stuff like that." They left the class together. Teresa asked him if he would help her with her French.

"Sure, anytime," Victor said.

"I won't be bothering you, will I?"

"Oh no, I like being bothered."

"*Bonjour*," Teresa said, leaving him outside her next class. She smiled and pushed wisps of hair from her face.

"Yeah, right, *bonjour*," Victor said. He turned and headed to his class. The rosebushes of shame on his face became bouquets of love. Teresa is a great girl, he thought. And Mr. Bueller is a good guy.

He raced to metal shop. After metal shop there was biology, and after biology a long sprint to the public library, where he checked out three French textbooks.

He was going to like seventh grade.

THE STRUGGLE FOR AN EDUCATION

from UP FROM SLAVERY:
AN AUTOBIOGRAPHY
by Booker T. Washington
illustrated by Marcy Ramsey

Booker T. Washington
as a young man.

Booker T. Washington was born a slave in Virginia in 1856. After being freed, he moved with his family to West Virginia. He taught himself how to read from an old spelling book that his mother found, and he went for lessons at a night school while working days at a salt refinery. Later, he worked at a coal mine. When he heard about a new school in Virginia for African Americans, the Hampton Normal and Agricultural Institute, he resolved to find a way to go there. In order to earn the money he needed, he took a job as a servant in the home of the mine owners, Mr. and Mrs. Ruffner, for a salary of five dollars a month.

Notwithstanding my success at Mrs. Ruffner's I did not give up the idea of going to the Hampton Institute. In the fall of 1872 I determined to make an effort to get there, although, as I have stated, I had no definite idea of the direction in which Hampton was, or of what it would cost to go there. I do not think that any one thoroughly sympathized with me in my ambition to go to Hampton unless it was my mother, and she was troubled with a grave fear that I was starting out on a "wild-goose chase." At any rate, I got only a half-hearted consent from her that I might start. The small amount of money that I had earned had been consumed by my stepfather and the remainder of the family, with the exception of a very few dollars, and so I had very little with which to buy clothes and pay my travelling expenses. My brother John helped me all that he could, but of course that was not a great deal, for his work was in the coal-mine, where he did not earn much, and most of what he did earn went in the direction of paying the household expenses.

Perhaps the thing that touched and pleased me most in connection with my starting for Hampton was the interest that many of the older coloured people took in the matter. They had spent the best days of their lives in slavery, and hardly expected to live to see the time when they would see a member of their race leave home to attend a boarding-school. Some of these older people would give me a nickel, others a quarter, or a handkerchief.

Finally the great day came, and I started for Hampton. I had only a small, cheap satchel that contained what few articles of clothing I could get. My mother at the time was rather weak and broken in health. I hardly expected to see her again, and thus our parting was all the more sad. She, however, was very brave through it all. At that time there were no through trains connecting that part of West Virginia with eastern Virginia. Trains ran only a portion of the way, and the remainder of the distance was travelled by stage-coaches.

The distance from Malden to Hampton is about five hundred miles. I had not been away from home many hours before it began to grow painfully evident that I did not have enough money to pay my fare to Hampton. One experience I shall long remember. I had been travelling over the mountains most of the afternoon in an old-fashioned stage-coach, when, late in the evening, the coach stopped for the night at a common, unpainted house called a hotel.

All the other passengers except myself were whites. In my ignorance I supposed that the little hotel existed for the purpose of accommodating the passengers who travelled on the stage-coach. The difference that the colour of one's skin would make I had not thought anything about. After all the other passengers had been shown rooms and were getting ready for supper, I shyly presented myself before the man at the desk. It is true I had practically no money in my pocket with which to pay for bed or food, but I had hoped in some way to beg my way into the good graces of the landlord, for at that season in the mountains of Virginia the weather was cold, and I wanted to get indoors for the night. Without asking as to whether I had any money, the man at the desk firmly refused to even consider the matter of providing me with food or lodging. This was my first experience in finding out what the colour of my skin meant. In some way I managed to keep warm by walking about, and so got through the night.

My whole soul was so bent upon reaching Hampton that I did not have time to cherish any bitterness toward the hotel-keeper.

By walking, begging rides both in wagons and in the cars, in some way, after a number of days, I reached the city of Richmond, Virginia, about eighty-two miles from Hampton. When I reached there, tired, hungry, and dirty, it was late in the night. I had never been in a large city, and this rather added to my misery. When I reached Richmond, I was completely out of money. I had not a single acquaintance in the place, and, being unused to city ways, I did not know where to go. I applied at several places for lodging, but they all wanted money, and that was what I did not have. Knowing nothing else better to do, I walked the streets. In doing this I passed by many food-stands where fried chicken and half-moon apple pies were piled high and made to present a most tempting appearance. At that time it seemed to me that I would have promised all that I expected to possess in the future to have gotten hold of one of those chicken legs or one of those pies. But I could not get either of these, nor anything else to eat.

I must have walked the streets till after midnight. At last I became so exhausted that I could walk no longer. I was tired, I was hungry, I was everything but discouraged. Just about the time when I reached extreme physical exhaustion, I came upon a portion of a street where the board sidewalk was considerably elevated. I waited for a few minutes, till I was sure that no passers-by could see me, and then crept under the sidewalk and lay for the night upon the ground, with my satchel of clothing for a pillow. Nearly all night I could hear the tramp of feet over my head. The next morning I found myself somewhat refreshed, but I was extremely hungry, because it had been a long time since I had had sufficient food. As soon as it became light enough for me to see my surroundings I noticed that I was near a large ship, and that this ship seemed to be unloading a cargo of pig iron. I went at once to the vessel and asked the captain to permit me to help unload the vessel in order to get money for food. The captain, a white man, who seemed to be kindhearted, consented. I worked long enough to earn money for my breakfast, and it seems to me, as I remember it now, to have been about the best breakfast that I have ever eaten.

My work pleased the captain so well that he told me if I desired I could continue working for a small amount per day. This I was very glad to do. I continued working on this vessel for a number of days. After buying food with the small wages I received there was not much left to add to the amount I

must get to pay my way to Hampton. In order to economize in every way possible, so as to be sure to reach Hampton in a reasonable time, I continued to sleep under the same sidewalk that gave me shelter the first night I was in Richmond. Many years after that the coloured citizens of Richmond very kindly tendered me a reception at which there must have been two thousand people present. This reception was held not far from the spot where I slept the first night I spent in that city, and I must confess that my mind was more upon the sidewalk that first gave me shelter than upon the reception, agreeable and cordial as it was.

When I had saved what I considered enough money with which to reach Hampton, I thanked the captain of the vessel for his kindness, and started again. Without any unusual occurrence I reached Hampton, with a surplus of exactly fifty cents with which to begin my education. To me it had been a long, eventful journey; but the first sight of the large, three-story, brick school building seemed to have rewarded me for all that I had undergone in order to reach the place. If the people who gave the money to provide that building could appreciate the influence the sight of it had upon me, as well as upon thousands of other youths, they would feel all the more encouraged to make such gifts. It seemed to me to be the largest and most beautiful building I had ever seen. The sight of it seemed to give me a new life. I felt that a new kind of existence had now begun—that life would now have a new meaning. I felt that I had reached the promised land, and I resolved to let no obstacle prevent me from putting forth the highest effort to fit myself to accomplish the most good in the world.

As soon as possible after reaching the grounds of the Hampton Institute, I presented myself before the head teacher for assignment to a class. Having been so long without proper food, a bath and change of clothing, I did not, of course, make a very favourable impression upon her, and I could see at once that there were doubts in her mind about the wisdom of admitting me as a student. I felt that I could hardly blame her if she got the idea that I was a worthless loafer or tramp. For some time she did not refuse to admit me, neither did she decide in my favour, and I continued to linger about her, and to impress her in all the ways I could with my worthiness. In the meantime I saw her admitting other students, and that added greatly to my discomfort, for I felt, deep down in my heart, that I could do as well as they, if I could only get a chance to show what was in me.

After some hours had passed, the head teacher said to me: "The adjoining recitation-room needs sweeping. Take the broom and sweep it."

It occurred to me at once that here was my chance. Never did I receive an order with more delight. I knew that I could sweep, for Mrs. Ruffner had thoroughly taught me how to do that when I lived with her.

I swept the recitation-room three times. Then I got a dusting-cloth and I dusted it four times. All the woodwork around the walls, every bench, table, and desk, I went over four times with my dusting-cloth. Besides, every piece of furniture had been moved and every closet and corner in the room had been thoroughly cleaned. I had the feeling that in a large measure my future depended upon the impression I made upon the teacher in the cleaning of that room. When I was through, I reported to the head teacher. She was a "Yankee" woman who knew just where to look for dirt. She went into the room and inspected the floor and closets; then she took her handkerchief and rubbed it on the woodwork about the walls, and over the table and benches. When she was unable to find one bit of dirt on the floor, or a particle of dust on any of the furniture, she quietly remarked, "I guess you will do to enter this institution."

I was one of the happiest souls on earth. The sweeping of that room was my college examination, and never did any youth pass an examination for entrance into Harvard or Yale that gave him more genuine satisfaction. I have passed several examinations since then, but I have always felt that this was the best one I ever passed.

FINE ART
LEARNING

Reading Le Figaro. 1883. Mary Cassatt.

Oil on canvas. Private collection. Photo: Bridgeman Art Library/Art Resource

Tree of Knowledge. 1978. Terry Chacon and Josefina Quezada.

Mural. Anthony Quinn Public Library, Los Angeles, California. Photo: © Michael Grecco/Sygma

St. Gregory and the scribes.
10th century.

Carved ivory bookcover. Kunsthistorisches
Museum, Vienna

The Music Lesson. c. 1665. Johannes Vermeer.

Oil on canvas. The Royal Collection, © 1993 Her Majesty Queen Elizabeth II

The Library. 1960.
Jacob Lawrence.

Tempera on fiberboard. Gift of
S.C. Johnson & Son, Inc.,
National Museum of American
Art, Smithsonian Institution,
Washington, D.C. © 1993
Jacob Lawrence/VAGA, NY.
Photo: Art Resource

A REAL JOB

from LITTLE BY LITTLE:
A WRITER'S EDUCATION by Jean Little
illustrated by Ellen Beier

I wanted to be a writer. But I had been told over and over again that you could not make a living as a writer. You had to get a real job and write in your spare time.

But what real job could a legally blind girl with a B.A. in English do?

Then I learned that the Rotary Crippled Children's Centre planned to start a small class for handicapped children and would need a teacher for it. I had no teaching qualifications, but I had worked with children with motor handicaps for three summers at Woodeden Camp.

The Rotarians agreed to hire me if I would first go to Montreal for two weeks to take a course on educating children with motor handicaps. The course was taught by Ellen Thiel from the Institute for Special Education at the University of Utah in Salt Lake City. I was intimidated by the other students, most of whom were experienced teachers and, although I enjoyed the course itself, I decided I would have to give up the idea of being a teacher. They kept talking a language I did not understand. Phonics, for instance. It was clearly of paramount importance, and I did not know what it meant. When I went in for my final interview, I explained all this to Ellen.

She laughed. "Phonics notwithstanding, I think you just may be a born teacher. I'm about to give a six-week course in Salt Lake on teaching children with motor handicaps. How would you like to come home to Utah with me and we could find out if I'm right?"

I stared at her, not knowing for a second whether or not she was kidding. Then I saw her grin. It was very friendly and had in it the same challenge that Dad's had had so often.

"All right," I said dazedly. "Where's Utah?"

I called home half an hour later to tell Mother that I was coming home to pack tomorrow and, the day after, was meeting this strange woman, Ellen Thiel, in Urbana and setting out for the American West.

"Wonderful," Mother said after only the shortest of hesitations. "I'll be there to meet you. You can tell me all about it while we pack."

At the end of that summer, I made a list in my diary of all the "new experiences" I had had since I left home. There are forty-nine items listed. I stopped only because I had filled the last page in that diary.

I did discover what Phonics meant, but I learned far more than that. The children in the demonstration class taught me a lot. So did Ellen's three children, Paula, Mary and Joe.

One evening I was reading *The Secret Garden* to the Thiel kids. Paula and Mary were enthralled by the story, but Joe kept fiddling with odds and ends on his bed and behaving as though he were extremely bored. When I closed the book, however, and started to shepherd the girls out of his room, he demanded that I give him the phone.

"Why?" I asked. "It's time you went to sleep. I read two extra chapters because the girls were so interested."

"I have to tell Mama something," Joe said.

Ellen was working late at the university. But I knew she was alone and besides, who was I to come between a boy and his mother?

I handed him the telephone on its long cord. Returning after tucking in the girls, I heard him say in a voice filled with wonder and delight, "Mum, they got into the garden!!!"

Never again did I make the mistake of thinking that a child who appeared inattentive was getting nothing out of a book.

His tone held exactly the joy Mary Lennox herself felt when she stepped through the ivy-covered green door.

At the end of the summer, Ellen wrote me a glowing letter of recommendation, and I went back to Guelph to start preparing for my teaching job at the Crippled Children's Centre.

I was not an ideal teacher. When your students continually correct your arithmetic, it keeps you humble. But I did one important thing well. I read to them.

I found that these were deprived children, not because they were not loved, but because they had largely been kept indoors due to their handicaps. Not one of them had ever seen a rainbow or been to a circus. They could not swim. They had not been taken to a zoo. Most of them had not ridden on a city bus. None had been on a train journey. Most had never eaten in a restaurant.

We did all these things, and Phonics, too.

Remembering how I had never found a cross-eyed heroine in a book, I decided to search for books about children with motor handicaps. I did not for one moment intend to limit my students to reading about crippled kids. I knew that they completely identified with Anne Shirley and Homer Price, that they actually became Bambi, Piglet and Wilbur. I did not think they needed a book to help them adjust. I did believe, however, that crippled children had a right to find themselves represented in fiction.

I began to search.

I found a book about a girl with polio. None of my students had polio. The Salk vaccine had already been discovered. I found several books that contained invalid children who completely recovered before the book ended. None of my students was ever going to recover completely.

I was looking for a book in which the child's handicap was present only in the background. The kids I taught were not conscious of their disabilities most of the time. They minded when people stared at them, or when their brothers and sisters got bicycles, of course. But usually they were too busy living to brood. Physio and occupational therapy were like arithmetic and reading, an accepted part of their days.

When we read *The Secret Garden*, Alec said, "What's the matter with Colin? Why doesn't he have therapy?"

"I guess it was written too long ago for them to know about therapy," I said weakly.

"What I can't figure out," Clifford complained, "is how he stood up for the first time in June and was well enough to beat Mary in a race by August. That's crazy."

The others loved the ending so much that they defended Colin's rapid recovery. But even they sounded a bit dubious.

We went through the same questions when we read *Heidi*. Clara got well even faster than Colin.

"Miss Little, what was wrong with Clara?"

It didn't say. I began to feel angry on their behalf.

Why couldn't there be a happy ending without a miracle cure? Why wasn't there a story with a child in it who resembled the kids I taught?

Somebody should write one, I thought.

It did not yet cross my mind that that somebody might be me.

MEET JEAN LITTLE, AUTHOR

*Jean Little's mother taught her to read as a small child,
and reading and writing remained the most important things in
Little's life. She explains: "When I was a child, because of my
limited vision and because my eyes looked peculiar, I was teased
a lot and left out of games. I did not feel unloved though,
because our family was a close one and because I found so
many friends in the books I read. I went to the library every single day, unless I was sick in bed—and then I sent my mother.*

*"When I wasn't reading, I was making up a story in my head. . . .
I was twelve when I began to write poems. My father gave me much criticism,
attention, and praise. He . . . told me, in no uncertain terms, that I was
going to be a writer."*

STORKS

from THE WHEEL ON THE SCHOOL
by Meindert DeJong
illustrated by Maurice Sendak

To start with there was Shora. Shora was a fishing village in Holland. It lay on the shore of the North Sea in Friesland, tight against the dike. Maybe that was why it was called Shora. It had some houses and a church and tower. In five of those houses lived the six school children of Shora, so that is important. There were a few more houses, but in those houses lived no children—just old people. They were, well, just old people, so they weren't too important. There were more children, too, but young children, toddlers, not school children—so that is not so important either.

The six children of Shora all went to the same little school. There was Jella; he was the biggest of the six. He was big and husky for his age. There was Eelka. He was slow and clumsy, except his mind; his mind was swift. There was Auka, and right here at the beginning there is nothing much to say about Auka—he was just a nice, everyday boy. You could have fun with him. There were Pier and Dirk; they were brothers. Pier and Dirk looked about as much alike as second cousins. But Pier liked what Dirk liked, and Dirk did what Pier did. They liked to be together. They were twins.

Then there was Lina. She was the only girl in the little Shora school. One girl with five boys. Of course, there was also a teacher, a man teacher.

Maybe to begin with, we really should have started with Lina. Not because she was the only schoolgirl in Shora, but because she wrote a story about storks. There were no storks in Shora. Lina had written this story about storks of her own accord—the teacher hadn't asked her to write it. In fact, until Lina read it out loud to the five boys and the teacher, nobody in school had even thought about storks.

But there one day, right in the middle of the arithmetic lesson, Lina raised her hand and asked, "Teacher, may I read a little story about storks? I wrote it all myself, and it's about storks."

Lina called it a story, but it was really an essay, a composition. The teacher was so pleased that Lina had written a little piece of her own accord, he stopped the arithmetic lesson right there and let Lina read her story. She began with the title and read on:

DO YOU KNOW ABOUT STORKS?

Do you know about storks? Storks on your roof bring all kinds of good luck. I know this about storks; they are big and white and have long yellow bills and tall yellow legs. They build great big messy nests, sometimes right on your roof. But when they build a nest on the roof of a house, they bring good luck to that house and to the whole village that that house stands in. Storks do not sing. They make a noise like you do when you clap your hands when you feel happy and good. I think storks clap their bills to make the happy sounds when they feel happy and good. They clap their bills almost all the time except when they are in the marshes and ditches hunting for frogs and little fishes and things. Then they are quiet. But on your roof they are noisy. But it is a happy noise, and I like happy noises.

That is all I know about storks; but my aunt in the village of Nes knows a lot about storks, because every year two big storks come to build their nest right on her roof. But I do not know much about storks, because storks never come to Shora. They go to all the villages all around, but they never come to Shora. That is the most that I know about storks, but if they came to Shora, I would know more about storks.

After Lina had finished reading her story, the room was quiet. The teacher stood there looking proud and pleased. Then he said, "That was a fine story, Lina. A very fine composition, and you know quite a lot about storks!" His eyes were pleased and bright. He turned to big Jella. "Jella," he said, "what do you know about storks?"

"About storks, Teacher?" Jella said slowly. "About storks—nothing." He looked surly and stubborn, because he felt stupid. He thought he ought to explain. "You see," he told the teacher, "I can't bring them down with my slingshot. I've tried and tried, but I just can't seem to do it."

The teacher looked startled. "But why would you want to shoot them down?"

"Oh, I don't know," Jella said. He wriggled a little in his seat. He looked unhappy. "Because they move, I guess."

"Oh," the teacher said. "Pier," he said then, "Dirk, what do you twins know about storks?"

"About storks?" Pier asked. "Nothing."

"Dirk," the teacher said.

"Just the same as Pier," Dirk said. "Nothing."

"Pier," the teacher said, "if I had asked Dirk first, what would have been your answer?"

"The same as Dirk's," Pier answered promptly. "Teacher, that's the trouble with being twins—if you don't know something, you don't know it double."

The teacher and the room liked that. It made everybody laugh. "Well, Auka," the teacher said, "how about you?"

Auka was still chuckling and feeling good about what Pier had said, but now he looked serious. "All I know is that if storks make happy noises with their bills like Lina said in her story, then I would like storks, too."

The teacher looked around and said: "Well, Eelka, there in the corner, that leaves only you."

Eelka thought awhile. "I'm like Lina, Teacher; I know little about storks. But if storks would come to Shora, then I think I would learn to know a lot about storks."

"Yes, that is true," the teacher said. "But now what do you think would happen if we all began to think a lot about storks? School's almost out for today, but if, from now until tomorrow morning when you come back to school, you thought and thought about storks, do you think things would begin to happen?"

They all sat still and thought that over. Eelka raised his hand. "But I'm afraid I can't think much about storks when I don't know much about storks. I'd be through in a minute."

Everybody laughed, but the teacher's eyes weren't pleased. "True, true," he said. "That's right, Eelka. We can't think much when we don't know much. But we can wonder! From now until tomorrow morning when you come to school again, will you do that? Will you wonder why and wonder why? Will you wonder why storks don't come to Shora to build their nests on the roofs, the way they do in all the villages around? For sometimes when we wonder, we can make things begin to happen.

"If you'll do that—then school is out right now!"

There they were out in the schoolyard—free! Jella peered again over the roofs on the houses at the distant tower rising beside the dike. He couldn't believe it. But the big white face of the tower clock spelled out three—a little past three. "Boy," Jella said in wonderment, "he let us out almost a whole hour early, just because of storks." Jella was beginning to appreciate storks. "What'll we do?" he said eagerly to the other boys.

But Lina took charge. Since she had started it with her essay about storks, she felt responsible. It was a wonderful day, the sky was bright and blue, the dike was sunny. "Let's all go and sit on the dike and wonder why, just like the teacher said."

Nobody objected. They all dutifully set out for the dike, still feeling happy because of the hour of freedom that had so suddenly and unexpectedly come to them. Still grateful enough to the storks and Lina to be obedient to her and sit on the dike and think about storks. But Jella lagged behind, and that was unusual. Big Jella was generally in the lead. Going down the village street he stared at every house he passed as if they were something new in the new freedom. But he dutifully climbed the dike and dutifully sat down at the end of the row of boys. Lina sat at the other end.

They sat. Nobody seemed to know just how to begin to wonder without the teacher there to start them off. Jella stared up at the sky. There wasn't a cloud in the sky. There were no

storks. There wasn't even a gull. Jella looked at the sea
stretching empty before him—there wasn't a ship in the sea.

Jella looked along the quiet row. Everybody was just sitting, hugging his knees. Everybody looked quiet and awk-
ward and uncomfortable. Suddenly Jella had had enough.
He looked along the row of boys at Lina. "The teacher didn't
say we had to sit in a row on the dike to wonder, did he?"

"No," Lina said, "but I thought, well, he's never given us
a whole hour off from school before, and I thought . . ."

"Well, then," Jella said . . . It just didn't feel right to sit
when you were free. But the quiet sea and the quiet sky suggested nothing to him. Then fortunately a slow canalboat
came pushing around a faraway bend in the canal. The two
men on deck lowered the sail and the mast, so the boat could
slide under the low bridge. The men picked up poles to push
the boat along under the bridge. Jella jumped up. Now he
had an idea. "Hey, let's all go get our poles and go ditch
jumping!"

All the boys, with the exception of Eelka, jumped up eagerly. Here was something to do—fun in the freedom.

"You, too, Eelka. Run and get your pole," Jella said. "And tell Auka to get mine, too. I'll wait here."

Lina stared at Jella in dismay. Even Eelka had to go. When it came to ditch jumping, Eelka generally was left out—he was too fat and slow and clumsy. "But I thought we were going to wonder why storks don't come to Shora?" Lina said. If even Eelka had to go along, she was going to be left behind all alone.

Lina glared down the dike after the running boys. "All right for you, Eelka," she yelled unhappily. She looked darkly at Jella. "Boy, if the teacher finds out that you . . ." She swallowed her words. It was a bitter, lost feeling to be left behind all alone in the surprise free hour.

Lina had a sudden hopeful thought. It must be that Jella wanted them all in on the ditch jumping, so that if the teacher found out, they'd all catch it together. Maybe he'd let her in on it, too! Maybe that was why he had stayed here with her on the dike. "Jella," Lina asked, "can I go, too? Why, if it wasn't for me, you'd be sitting in school right now. And I could get my mother's clothes pole. It's long and smooth and . . ."

"Naw," Jella said immediately. "Girls are no good at jumping. It's a boy's game."

"I'd be just as good as Eelka. Better even," Lina said indignantly.

"Yeah, I guess so. But Eelka doesn't mind getting wet, but girls worry about wet feet and their dresses flying. And they squeal and scream, and then they get scared and go giggly."

Jella seemed to have thought a lot about it. Lina could see it was totally no use wheedling or arguing. She drew her wooden shoes primly up under her, hugged her knees, and stared wretchedly out at the sea. "Teacher said we were to wonder why the storks don't come. He even said if we wondered really hard things might begin to happen."

"We'll wonder while we jump ditches," Jella said shortly. He was a bit uneasy. But now the boys were coming back, Auka with two vaulting poles. Jella started to leave. "And we don't care if you do tell the teacher! He didn't say we were supposed to sit like dopes on the dike."

So Jella did care—he was even worried she would tell. She was no tattletale! Lina did not deign to turn around to answer. But she couldn't help looking down the dike when Eelka came dragging his long vaulting pole. "All right, for you, Eelka," she said stormily.

That was the trouble with being the only girl: you got left out of things. And if Eelka didn't also get left out, there was nothing for her to do but sit by herself or play with her little sister Linda and the other little children. What was the fun of that? Well, she'd show them. She'd sit right here and think and wonder really hard. Tomorrow morning when the teacher asked, up would go her hand, but there they'd all sit stupid and with their mouths full of teeth. It did not seem much of a threat. The excited voices of the boys came drifting back to her.

Lina fixed her eyes hard upon a distant hazy swirling far out above the sea, wanting it to be a stork but knowing all the time it was just a sea gull. She wouldn't play with Eelka again for a week! Maybe ten days even, maybe three weeks!

Even if in all that time Jella and the rest left Eelka out of every one of their games. She wouldn't bother with Eelka either. She just wouldn't bother!

She stared hard at the gull. It was still a gull; it wasn't a stork. Suppose a whole big flock of storks came flying up out of the sea. The boys, jumping ditches, wouldn't even see them. But Lina had to admit to herself it wouldn't make much difference if they saw the storks or not. The storks wouldn't stay in Shora, and the boys couldn't make them stay, so what was the difference. Lina sighed. It was hard being the only girl in Shora.

She took off one of her wooden shoes and sat staring moodily into it. She caught herself doing it. It was a lonely habit. She often sat staring into her shoe. It somehow made her feel better and seemed to help her to think better, but she didn't know why. She often wished she could wear her wooden shoes in the schoolroom instead of just socks. The wooden shoes had to be left out in the portal. Lina was sure it would help no end if she could pull off one of her shoes and stare and dream into it awhile—especially before doing an arithmetic problem. Lina sighed. You couldn't dream with arithmetic. With arithmetic you could only think. It made arithmetic sort of scary. Hard and scary and not very exciting.

Storks were exciting! "Wonder why? Wonder why?" Lina said quite hard into her wooden shoe. The words came bouncing back at her out of the hard wooden shell. She whispered it into the shoe; the words came whispering back. She sat dreaming, staring into the shoe. And the sea gull was swirling and sailing far out at sea.

Still thinking and dreaming about storks, she got up in her nice hazy daze and wandered away from the dike, one shoe in her hand. She went slowly down the street, staring intently at the roofs of all the houses as if she'd never seen them before. The village street lay quiet and empty. Lina had it to herself all the way through the village to the little school. The school had the sharpest roof of all, Lina decided. All the roofs were sharp, but the school's was the sharpest.

A thin faraway shout and a shrill laugh came through to her. She turned. In the far, flat distance she could see the boys. Now big Jella, it must be Jella, went sailing high over a ditch. Hard behind him, first sprinting, then sailing high on their poles, came the other three boys. And then there came one more; it must be Eelka. But Eelka disappeared—he must have gone into the ditch. Now there was a lot of shouting and running. Lina caught herself waiting anxiously for Eelka to appear out of the ditch. Then she remembered that she wasn't going to play with Eelka for three weeks. She turned her back to the distant boys. "I hope he went in up to his neck," she heard herself saying half-aloud. It surprised her. For now it didn't matter whether or not Eelka went into the water up to his neck; it didn't matter that the boys were having fun. She knew why the storks didn't come to build their nests in Shora. The roofs were all too sharp! But not only did she know the reason why, she also knew what to do about it! They had to put a wagon wheel on top of one of the roofs—a wagon wheel just like her aunt in Nes had on her roof. Tomorrow morning she would spring it on them in the schoolroom. They'd be surprised!

Lina started to hurry back to the village, almost as if she had to hurry to tell someone. She put her wooden shoe back on to hurry better. There wasn't anyone there, she knew. The boys were playing in the fields; the teacher had gone. She could go home and tell her mother, but she would tell her mother anyway. It just seemed to her there had to be some-body *new* to tell it to—she had that feeling. There wasn't any-one like that. The whole street lay empty. It made her hurrying suddenly seem senseless. Lina slowed herself by star-ing at a house.

Once more Lina dawdled down the street, once more she stood a dreamy while before each house. Her shoe came off again. She was staring up at the roof of Grandmother Sibble III's house when the old lady came out. It startled Lina.

"I know I'm a nosy old creature," Grandmother Sibble III said, "but there you stand again, staring. I've been watching you wandering from the dike to the school and back again like a little lost sheep."

Lina laughed a polite little laugh. "Oh, I'm not exactly wandering. I'm wondering."

"Oh," said the old lady, mystified. "Well, I guess wondering is always better than wandering. It makes more sense." She chuckled a nice little old lady's chuckle.

They looked at each other. And Lina thought how she had never talked much to Grandmother Sibble III except to say a polite "hello" as she walked by. Now she did not know just what to say to her.

The old lady was still looking at her curiously. "Is that why you have your shoe in your hand?" she said gently. "Because you were wondering so hard?"

In surprise Lina glanced down at her hand holding the wooden shoe. She reddened a little and hastily slipped it on her foot. What must Grandmother Sibble think—not that she was her grandmother, she was just the grandmother of the whole village, the oldest old lady. It certainly must have looked silly, her hobbling down the street on one shoe, carrying the other. No wonder Grandmother Sibble III had come out of the house!

"I . . ." Lina said, trying to explain. She giggled a little. "Oh, isn't it silly?" She fished in her mind for some sensible explanation. None would come. But Grandmother Sibble III wasn't standing there grinning in a superior, adult way. She just looked—well, mystified and inquisitive. Lina decided to tell her. "I guess it does look silly and odd, but it somehow helps me think better to look into my shoe. Then when I get to thinking really hard, I forget to put it back on again," she said defensively.

"Why, yes," the old lady said immediately. "Isn't it funny how odd little things like that help? Now I can think much better by sort of rocking myself and sucking on a piece of candy, and I've done it ever since I was a little girl like you." She carefully settled herself on the top step of her brick stoop. She looked as if she was settling herself for a good, long chat. "Now of course, I've just got to know what it was you were thinking about so hard it made you forget your shoe." She chuckled her little old chuckle again. "And if you don't tell me, I won't sleep all night from trying to guess."

They laughed together. Grandmother Sibble patted the stoop next to her. "Why don't you come and sit down with me and tell me about it."

Lina eagerly sat down—close, exactly where the old lady had patted. Old Grandmother Sibble was nice, she thought to herself. It was a nice surprise. She didn't talk to you as if you were a tiny tot, almost a baby, and miles of years away, the way grownups usually did. She even understood silly girl things like looking into a wooden shoe. She understood it the way a girl friend—if you had a girl friend—would understand. A girl friend who also had silly tricks and secretly told you about them. Aloud Lina said, "I was thinking about storks, Grandmother Sibble. Why storks don't come and build their nests in Shora."

Grandmother Sibble looked thoughtful. "Well, that is a thing to ponder all right. No wonder you had your shoe off. We here in Shora always without storks."

"But I figured out why," Lina told the old lady proudly. "Our roofs are too sharp!"

"Well, yes . . . Yes, I guess so," the old lady said carefully, sensing Lina's sharp excitement. "But that could be remedied by putting a wagon wheel on the roof, couldn't it? The way they do in the other villages?"

"Yes, I'd thought of that," Lina said promptly. "My aunt in Nes has a wagon wheel on her roof, and storks nest on it every year."

"Ah, yes," the old lady said, "but doesn't your aunt's house have trees around it, too?"

"Yes, it has," Lina said, looking in surprise at the little old lady. Why, Grandmother Sibble must have been thinking about storks, too. It seemed amazing, the old, old lady thinking about storks. "I guess I never thought about trees. Well, just because there are no trees in Shora—so I didn't think about trees." Lina's voice faded away. Here was a whole new thing to think about.

"Would a stork think about trees?" the old lady wanted to know. "It seems to me a stork would think about trees. And it seems to me that in order to figure out what a stork would want, we should try to think the way a stork would think."

Lina sat bolt upright. What a wonderful thing to say! Lina fumbled for her shoe while she eagerly looked at the old lady.

"You see, if I were a stork, even if I had my nest on a roof, I think I would still like to hide myself in a tree now and then and settle down in the shade and rest my long legs. Not be on the bare peak of a roof for everybody to see me all the time."

Lina pulled her feet up under her and looked down confusedly at her wooden shoes. She really needed her wooden shoe right now. Her thoughts were racing.

"You see, years ago," Grandmother Sibble was explaining, "oh, years and years ago when I was the only girl in Shora, the way you are the only girl now, there were trees in Shora and there were storks! The only trees in Shora grew on my grandmother's place. My grandmother was then the only grandmother of Shora. She was Grandmother Sibble I, just like I am now Grandmother Sibble III and you would someday be Grandmother Sibble IV if your mother had named you Sibble instead of Lina. I asked her to! Oh, I had no business asking—we're not even related—but it just seems there should always be a Grandmother Sibble in Shora. But that's beside the point.

"The point is, my grandmother's little house stood exactly where your school stands now but, oh, so different from your little naked school. Really different! My grandmother's house was roofed with reeds and storks like reeds. And my grandmother's house was hidden in trees. And storks like trees. Weeping willow trees grew around the edge of a deep moat that went all around my grandmother's house. And in the shadowy water under the hanging willows, pickerel swam in the moat. And over the moat there was a little footbridge leading right to my grandmother's door. And in one of the willows there was always a stork nest, and there was another nest on the low reed roof of my grandmother's house. As a little girl I used to stand on the footbridge and think that I could almost reach up to the low roof of the little house and touch the storks, so close they seemed."

"Oh, I didn't know. I never knew," Lina said breathlessly.

Grandmother Sibble did not seem to hear. Her eyes were looking far, far back. She shook her head. "A storm came," she said. "As storms so often come to Shora. But this was a real storm. The wind and waves roared up the dike for longer than a week. For a whole week the water pounded and the salt spray flew. The air was full of salt; you even tasted the salt on your bread in your houses. And when it was all done, there were only three willows left at Sibble's Corner—that is what they called my grandmother's house, because everybody gathered there of a warm summer day to sit and chat and rest from work in the only shade in Shora, to talk and to lean their tired backs against the only trees. Then even those three left-over trees sickened and died. I guess their leaves had just taken in too much salt that long week of the storm.

"Later, after Grandmother Sibble I died, they came and tore down her house and chopped out the old rotted stumps of the willows and filled the moat with dirt. Then there was nothing for years and years, until they built your naked little school on the same spot. But the storks never came back."

Lina sat wide-eyed, hugging her knees, staring straight ahead, drinking it in, dreaming it over—the things the old lady had said—dreaming the picture. It sounded like a far-away tale, and yet it had been! Grandmother Sibble III had seen it! She had thought as a little girl that she could reach up and touch the storks, it had been so real and so close. Right in Shora!

"I never knew. I never knew," Lina whispered to herself. "And even a little footbridge," she told herself and hugged her knees.

Grandmother Sibble III roused herself. "So you see you mustn't think our sharp roofs is the whole story, must you?" she said softly. "We must think about other things, too. Like our lack of trees, our storms, our salt spray. We must think about everything. And to think it right, we must try to think the way a stork would think!"

Grandmother Sibble said "we"!

"Then have you been thinking about storks, too?" Lina asked in astonishment.

"Ever since I was a little girl. And ever since then I've wanted them back. They're lucky and cozy and friendly and, well, just right. It's never seemed right again—the village without storks. But nobody ever did anything about it."

"Teacher says," Lina told the old lady softly, "that maybe if we wonder and wonder, then things will begin to happen."

"Is that what he said? Ah, but that is so right," the old lady said. "But now you run in the house. There's a little tin on my kitchen shelf and in it there are wineballs. You get us each a wineball out of the tin. Then I'll sit on my stoop and you sit on yours, and we'll think about storks. But we'll think better each on his own stoop, because often thinking gets lost in talking. And maybe your teacher is right—that if we begin to think and wonder, somebody will begin to make things happen. But you go find the candy tin; I can think much better sucking on a wineball. And you take one, too. You watch if it doesn't work much better than looking inside an old wooden shoe."

Lina had never been in Grandmother Sibble III's house before, never in the neat kitchen. There was the shelf, and there was the candy tin. There were storks on the candy tin!

Pictures of storks in high sweeping trees were all around the four sides of the candy tin. On the lid was a village, and on every house there was a huge, ramshackle stork nest. In every nest tall storks stood as though making happy noises with their bills up into a happy blue sky.

Lina kept turning the candy tin to see the pictures again and again. Suddenly she woke up to the fact that she was staying in Grandmother Sibble's house a long, long time. Her first time in Grandmother Sibble's house, too! What would she think? She hastily shoved the candy tin back on its shelf and hurried to the stoop.

"Grandmother Sibble, storks on your candy tin! And on every roof a nest! Oh . . ." Suddenly Lina realized she'd forgotten the wineballs. She raced back. It was hard not to look at the storks, but she kept her face partly turned away and picked out two round, red wineballs. Then she ran back. "I forgot all about the wineballs," she apologized.

"Yes, I know," Grandmother Sibble said gently, for she saw that Lina—though looking straight at her while handing her her wineball—was not seeing her at all. Lina had dreams in her eyes. Lina was seeing storks on every roof in Shora. The old lady quietly let Lina wander off the stoop and to her own house. Lina had dreams in her eyes and would not hear words anyway.

On her own stoop Lina looked back for the first time. There sat Grandmother Sibble III rocking herself a little and sucking on her wineball. But the dream Lina was dreaming was not just about storks—not directly. Later she would think about storks, try to think the way a stork would think, as Grandmother Sibble had said. But now she thought about Grandmother Sibble, who had a candy tin in her house with storks on it and who had known storks and who, when she was a little girl, had imagined she could reach up and almost touch the storks.

But that was not the wonder either, not quite. The real wonder was that, just as the teacher had said, things *had* begun to happen. Begin to wonder why, the teacher had said, and maybe things will begin to happen. And they had! For there sat Grandmother Sibble III on the stoop of her little house, and suddenly she had become important. She wasn't just an old person any more, miles of years away, she was a friend. A friend, like another girl, who also wondered about storks.

Lina looked again at the little old lady, sitting there on the stoop. She marveled; she sat feeling nice and warm about a little old lady who had become a friend. It was a lovely feeling, as sweet as a wineball, as sweet as a dream. Lina took one shoe off and peered into it. Why, storks did bring good luck! The storks had made a friend for her. Why, now when the boys left her out of their games, she could go to Grandmother Sibble, and they would sit and talk and chat. Lina looked up out of the shoe triumphantly. Why, yes!

In the morning it was school again. There they were in the schoolroom again, the five boys and Lina and the teacher. But this Saturday morning they did not start out by singing the old, old song about the country—"my lovely

spot of ground, my fatherland, where once my cradle stood."
No, they sat quietly as the teacher stood looking at each one
of them in turn. And then he said, "Who wondered why?
And where did it lead you?"

Lina's hand shot up. To her amazement every hand shot up
with hers, even Jella's and Eelka's. The teacher looked so
happy and pleased about it, it made Lina furious. "Why,
Teacher, they never did! They went ditch jumping."

She clapped her hand to her mouth, but it was too late.
She wasn't a tattletale. It was just that it had come boiling up
out of her, because it had made her so furious. They were
fooling the teacher, and it was making him happy.

The teacher looked at her a short moment. He seemed surprised. He turned away from her to Jella. Jella sat there in the
front seat, big and stubborn and angry. He was really angry
with her. But the teacher was saying, "Well, Jella, and what
did you think was the reason why storks do not come to
Shora?"

"Oh, I didn't think," Jella told the teacher honestly. "I
asked my mother."

The teacher smiled. "Well, next to thinking, asking is the
way to become wise. What did your mother say?"

"She said storks don't come to Shora because they never
did. She said storks go back every year to the same nesting
spots. So if they never came to Shora, they never will. So
there's just nothing to be done about it, she said."

Lina sat in her seat, trembling with eagerness to tell them
that storks had once come to Shora, to tell them what
Grandmother Sibble had said. She wanted to wave her hand
frantically. But all the boys were angry with her, and even

the teacher had been surprised and disappointed. It was a woebegone feeling, but still she had to do something. She quivered with eagerness. Then she *was* waving her hand, almost getting up out of her seat, but the teacher didn't take notice. She had to tell them! Lina heard herself saying out loud, "Oh, but storks did once upon a time come to Shora!"

They all turned to her, even the teacher. The next moment Lina was excitedly telling the room the story that Grandmother Sibble had told her about Sibble's Corner and the storks and the willow trees all around and the moat with the footbridge. About storks right here in the exact spot where the school now stood! She even told about the pickerel in the moat.

Jella in the front seat turned right around when he heard about the pickerel. He forgot he was angry with her; he forgot he was in school. He just said right out loud, without permission, "Oh, boy, pickerel! Were they big, Lina?"

All the boys had big excited eyes. They seemed to be much more interested in the pickerel than in the storks. All but Eelka. Eelka raised his hand, and now he was saying in his slow way, "What Lina said about trees. You know, Teacher, that is exactly what I thought when I wondered why. Storks don't come to Shora because we have no trees!"

Eelka's desk was next to Lina's. She twisted in her seat to stare at him. How did he dare? He'd wondered why! He'd gone jumping ditches!

It was as if Eelka knew what she was thinking, for he calmly told the teacher, "I don't suppose I would have thought of trees. It was really when I jumped right smack into the middle of a ditch and went under that I thought of it. I really got soaked, and I wished there was a tree to hang my clothes on. But there aren't any trees, so I had to go home dripping wet. Boy, did I catch it from my mother!"

The teacher laughed as long and hard as the class. Even Lina had to laugh.

"Well, Eelka," the teacher said, "even though you had to do your thinking under water, it was still good thinking." His eyes were bright with laughter as he turned to the class. "All right, now. Does everyone agree with Eelka that the number one reason why storks do not come to Shora is because we have no trees?" He turned to the blackboard and wrote in big letters:

THE REASONS WHY STORKS
DO NOT COME TO SHORA

Under the words he put a big number one and waited.

"I still think the number one reason is what my mother said," Jella spoke up.

"Ah, but Lina has just told us that storks used to come to Shora. In fact, Jella, Grandmother Sibble III has seen storks nesting above the spot where you are sitting now. Where our school now stands. Imagine it!" said the teacher.

"I guess maybe my mother was wrong," Jella said slowly. He seemed to hate to have to admit it. He looked up at the ceiling in a troubled way.

Then Auka raised his hand and quietly said, "Then the number one reason is still NO TREES."

"That's what Grandmother Sibble thinks, too," Lina told the class honestly. "She says storks like shelter and trees and hiding and a shady place to rest their long legs. She said she

would if she were a stork! And Grandmother Sibble told me the way to find out what a stork would want is to try to think like a stork."

The teacher stood looking at Lina. "Is that what Grandmother Sibble III told you? I think that is wonderful," he said. He turned back to the class. "Well, are we agreed then that the number one reason for no storks in Shora is no trees?" He turned toward the board with his chalk as if to write it down.

Lina frantically waved her hand to stop him. "Not trees— roofs!" she almost shouted when the teacher did not turn. "Teacher," she said desperately to the teacher's back, "even though Grandmother Sibble and everybody thinks it is trees, it has to be roofs. Storks don't just build nests in trees, they build their nests on roofs, too. But our roofs in Shora are too sharp! Oh, it just has to be roofs," she pleaded. "Because we can put wheels on the roofs for storks to build their nests on, but we can't do anything soon about trees." Breathlessly she told the class about Grandmother Sibble's candy tin with the picture of a whole village on its lid and stork nests on every roof—because there was a wheel on every roof for the storks to build their nests on!

Pier and Dirk said almost together, "Oh, man, imagine a nest on every roof in Shora!"

"Even on the roof of our school!" Auka shouted.

"But that's just it. That's just it!" Lina all but shouted at them. "There's not a single wheel on any roof in Shora, because, just like Grandmother Sibble, everybody else must have figured it was no trees. So nobody ever put up a wheel. Nobody even tried! But how can we know if we don't try?"

Lina sat back waiting breathlessly, hopefully looking at the teacher. Oh, she had to be right! Teacher had to think it was right.

The teacher liked their excitement. He stood before the blackboard turning the piece of chalk in his hand in no hurry to write anything down. He looked at the boys who were still looking in surprise at Lina. He looked at Lina. "Aha," he said proudly. "Little Lina." And then he wrote on the blackboard Lina's reason in big white letters:

NO WHEELS ON OUR SHARP ROOFS

He turned back to the class. "Could it be?" he asked. "If we put wheels on our sharp roofs, could there be storks on every roof in Shora, the way Lina saw it in the picture on the candy tin?"

"Aw, that was just a picture," Jella said, scornfully. "You can put anything in a picture. All that is is a dream."

"Ah, yes, that's all it is," the teacher said. "As yet! But there's where things have to start—with a dream. Of course, if you just go on dreaming, then it stays a dream and becomes stale and dead. But first to dream and then to do— isn't that the way to make a dream come true? Now sit for a moment, picture it for a moment: our Shora with trees and storks. Now Shora is bare, but try to see Shora with trees and storks and life. The blue sky above and the blue sea stretching behind the dike and storks flying over Shora. Do you see it?"

"Trees won't grow in Shora," Jella argued stubbornly. "It's the salt spray and the wind storms. There's only one tree in Shora, and that's a small cherry tree in the back yard of legless Janus. But the yard's got a high wall around it, so high you can hardly climb it. The cherry tree grows against the sunny wall of the house, and Janus pets it and guards it. He won't let a bird or a kid get even one cherry. Not one!"

"Well, but doesn't that show us something?" the teacher said. "That to raise trees in Shora we must perhaps protect them. And couldn't we raise trees that could withstand the storms and salt spray—stouter and stronger than willows? There must be trees that grow along the sea. Or maybe we would have to protect the willows with a windbreak of poplar trees. The point is, if trees once grew here, couldn't we make them do it again?"

"Oh, but that would take too long," Dirk said. "That would take years."

"Making dreams become real often takes long," the teacher said. "I don't mean that it should be done at once. Our first problem is how to make just one pair of storks come to nest in Shora. That is what we are trying to do right now by first thinking out the reasons why the storks don't nest in Shora. But after that . . . If trees once grew where our school now stands, wouldn't they grow there again? Think of it. Trees all around our school!"

"And a moat with pickerel in it," Jella promptly added. "We boys could even dig it ourselves, and Lina could make hot chocolate milk for the diggers."

"Yes, Jella, now you are getting into the spirit of it. For that matter, we could even plant our own little trees. But first, before we can even start to think of all that, what must we do?"

"Find a wheel to put on a roof," Lina promptly cried.

"Ah, hah," the teacher said. "Now we are getting to something that we can do. Now do you see? We wondered why and we reasoned it out. Now we must do. Now we must find a wagon wheel, and then we must put it up on a roof. But behind doing that lies the long dream—storks on every roof in Shora. Trees! Maybe even a moat around the school. Can you picture our Shora like that?"

Excitement was in his voice; excitement was in the whole room. Lina couldn't sit still. She squirmed and squirmed, and then her hand shot up. "And a footbridge leading right to the door! We'd go over the footbridge to school. Teacher," she pleaded. "Teacher, I could get Grandmother Sibble's candy tin. Then we could all see what Shora would be like with storks and trees."

The teacher nodded. "Run then, Lina."

Grandmother Sibble III had no objections whatever to Lina's taking the candy tin to school. "Oh, no, child, keep it there as long as you like. Keep it until you get real storks in Shora." She opened the tin and took out a wineball. "Why, enough left for a wineball for each of you."

In the schoolroom they passed the candy tin around from hand to hand, and each one looked at all the pictures on the sides and on the lid. Each took out one wineball before reluctantly passing the tin on. The teacher took out the last wineball and then put the candy tin on the top ledge of the blackboard, on its side, so that the village with the trees and the storks on every roof could be seen from every point in the room. And underneath the tin, he wrote on the blackboard in big letters: "COULD IT BE?"

He turned back to the class. "Imagine a zebra in Shora," he said. "Imagine the long necks of two giraffes poking over the top of the dike. Imagine a giraffe running along our dike."

"Imagine a lion in Shora!" Auka said.

"Yes, Auka, even imagine a lion in Shora," the teacher surprisingly agreed. "A good lion, a gentle lion in our street. But isn't it almost like that with storks? Do you know where our storks come from—where they are when they aren't in Holland? Imagine the heart of Africa. The head of a big river deep in Africa, where it isn't a river any more but little rivulets and reedy swampland and marshes that go to make the beginnings of a big river. That's where our storks are now. Right there among the zebras and the herds of gazelles, among the lions and the buffaloes. Do you see our stork? There's an old rhinoceros right behind him, skulking in the brush. Do you see the stork standing on the banks of the river where the river begins? Just beyond him in the swampy river is a herd of hippopotamuses, snorting and blowing in the deeper water. And the stork lives among them! Until a time comes and the big noble bird spreads his great wings, flaps his big wings, and comes out of the wilds of Africa to live among us. A great wild bird, yet tame and gentle, living among us in a village. Isn't it wonderful? And maybe, just maybe—It's still a dream. We haven't even a wheel as yet; we don't even know what roof we'll put it on."

"Oh, yes, we do! Oh, yes, we do!" the whole class shouted. "It's got to go right on the roof of our school."

"Why, yes," the teacher said. "Why, yes, class! Then who's going to look for a wagon wheel? Look for a wagon wheel where one is and where one isn't; where one could be and where one couldn't possibly be?"

They were all too breathless to say a word. But Jella hastily swallowed his wineball whole, then blurted it out for all of them. "We all are. From the moment school is out until we find one."

The teacher nodded and nodded. "That's how we'll begin to make a dream come true. We'll begin at noon. It's Saturday, and we

have our free afternoon before us. We'll
have a whole afternoon to try to find a
wagon wheel. We'll really work at it,
because that is how to start to make a
dream come true . . ."

MEET MAURICE SENDAK, ILLUSTRATOR

*As a child, Maurice Sendak was not happy in school. He says, "In order to
get there, I had to talk myself out of a state of panic nearly every day. I couldn't
stand being [shut up] with other children—I never did like competition—and I was
usually so embarrassed that I stammered."*

*Sendak did, however, come to appreciate books. He tells of the book he
received on his ninth birthday: "Back in the thirties I didn't have any 'official' children's books. (I refer to the classics.) The only thing I can remember is cheap
paperbacks, comic books . . . My sister bought me my first book, The Prince and
the Pauper. A ritual began with that book which I recall very clearly. The first
thing was to set it up on the table and stare at it for a long time. Not because I was*

*impressed with Mark Twain; it was just such a beautiful
object. Then came the smelling of it . . . it was printed on
particularly fine paper, unlike the Disney books I had gotten
previous to that, which were printed on very poor paper and
smelled poor . . . It also had a shiny cover, a laminated cover.
I flipped over that. And it was very solid. I mean, it was bound
very tightly. I remember trying to bite into it, which I don't
imagine is what my sister intended when she bought the book
for me. But the last thing I did with the book was to read it. It
was all right. But I think it started then, a passion for books
and bookmaking. I wanted to be an illustrator very early in my
life; to be involved in books in some way."*

SAM AT THE LIBRARY

Carol Combs Hole
illustrated by Nelle Davis

My librarian
Said to me,
"This is the best book for grade three."
That was the year I was in third,
So I took the book
On her good word.
I hurried home, crawled into bed,
Pulled up the covers over my head,
And turned my flashlight on
And read.

But the book was awful
And icky and bad.
It wasn't funny;
It wasn't sad.
It wasn't scary or terribly tragic,
And it didn't have even an ounce of magic!

No prince,
No dragon,
No talking cat;
Not even a witch in a pointy hat.
Well!
What can you do with a book like that?

My librarian
Tried once more:
"This is the best book for grade four."
That was the year I was in fourth,
So I took her word
For what it was worth;
And I took the book back home to bed,
Draped the covers over my head
Turned my flashlight on,
And read.

But the book was dull as a Brussels sprout.
I couldn't care how the story came out.
It didn't have baseball
Or football or tennis,
It didn't have danger and lurking menace,
Or wicked kings like the ones in history,
And it didn't have even an ounce of mystery!
No midnight moan,
No deserted shack,
No great detective hot on the track,
Nobody tortured on the rack.
So naturally
I took it back.

My librarian
Used her head.
When I was in grade five, she said,
"Sam, it's silly to try to pretend
You like the books I recommend,

When it's perfectly,
Patently,
Plain to see—
Your taste and mine will never agree.
You like sports books—
I can't stand them.
I don't like mysteries—
You demand them.
You think fairy tales are for babies.
You hate dog stories worse than rabies.
You're not me,
And I'm not you.
We're as different as pickles and stew.
So from now on, Sam,
You go to the shelf,
And pick out the books you want,
Yourself."

And ever since then
We get along fine.
She reads her books;
I read mine.
And if we choose to converse together,
We smile—
And talk about the weather.

TO YOUNG READERS

Gwendolyn Brooks
illustrated by Nelle Davis

Good books are
bandages
and voyages
and linkages to Light;

are keys and hammers,
ripe redeemers,
dials and bells and
healing hallelujah.

Good books are good
nutrition.
A reader is a Guest
nourished, by riches of the
Feast,
to lift, to launch, and to
applaud the world.

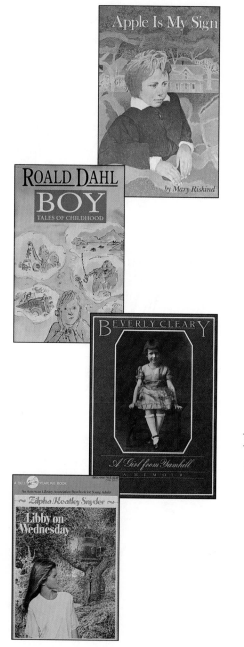

BIBLIOGRAPHY

Apple Is My Sign by Mary Riskind. Apple Harry, a ten-year-old deaf boy, goes to a special school in Philadelphia to learn how to speak.

Boy: Tales of Childhood by Roald Dahl. The author of *Charlie and the Chocolate Factory* and other popular books tells the sometimes sad and often hilarious story of his school years.

A Girl from Yamhill: A Memoir by Beverly Cleary. The author of *Dear Mr. Henshaw* and other books tells about her school years in Oregon.

Libby on Wednesday by Zilpha Keatley Snyder. An eleven-year-old girl learns how to work with others in a writer's workshop.

The Man Who Loved Books by Jean Fritz. Can you imagine how valuable books were when each book had to be printed by hand? This story of Saint Columba, who lived in Ireland about 1,500 years ago, will tell you.

Sideways Arithmetic from Wayside School by Louis Sachar. You'll have fun solving these wacky mathematical puzzles.

Top Secret by John Reynolds Gardiner. What if humans could use photosynthesis to make their own food, just as plants do? You'll laugh at this description of Allen Brewster's science project.

The Winning of Miss Lynn Ryan by Ilene Cooper. How can Carrie make a good impression on her attractive young teacher? In doing research for science and social studies projects, Carrie decides that it is more important to please herself than to please her teacher.

ASTRONOMY

HOW DID WE FIND OUT THE EARTH IS ROUND?

from the book by Isaac Asimov
illustrated by Stephen Marchesi

IS THE EARTH FLAT?

F ar back in ancient times, everybody thought the earth was flat. This is because it looks flat.

If you are in a boat way out in the middle of the ocean, the top of the water looks flat in every direction and the sky seems to fit over it like an upside-down bowl. The line where the sky and water meet is called the "horizon." The horizon looks like a circle with you yourself at the center.

If you are on land, the land stretches out to a horizon also. The horizon on land, however, is not even. It goes up and down because of houses, trees, hills, and other things.

Some ancient people suspected the earth went on forever. They thought it might be a huge flat piece of land and sea with no end at all.

But if this were the case, then what about the sun? The sun rose in the east in the morning. It traveled across the sky and set in the west in the evening. Then the next morning, it rose again in the east.

Some ancient people tried to explain this by saying that every morning a brand-new sun was manufactured and rose. When it set, it was destroyed.

Others said that the sun set in the ocean to the west. Then during the night, it was put in a boat and rowed to the east. By morning, it was ready to rise again.

Still others thought the sun was a golden, flaming chariot pulled by magic horses that could fly through the air. In the morning, the sun-god would get into the chariot in the east. Then he and his horses would climb through the air, reaching the top of the sky at noon. They would race downward, reaching the far western ground in the evening. Somehow the sun-god would get back to the east during the night when his golden, flaming chariot gave out no light.

Stars that were very far from the North Star moved in such big circles that those circles dipped below the horizon. Those stars rose in the east and set in the west.

The moon also traveled across the sky from east to west. So did the stars. These things had to be explained also. The ancient explanations just didn't make sense.

Suppose we have a flat earth stretching out in every direction. How deep is it? Suppose you begin to dig a hole. Can you keep on digging forever, going down and down without end?

Or is the earth just a slab of material, maybe a mile thick— or ten miles—or fifty miles? If it is just a slab of material, what keeps it from falling down?

The people who lived in India in ancient times decided the earth didn't fall because it was resting on huge elephants.

But what were the elephants standing on? They said all the elephants were standing on the back of a gigantic turtle.

And what was the turtle standing on? They said it was swimming in a tremendous ocean.

Well, then, did the ocean stretch all the way down? There was no answer to that.

So you see, while the earth *looks* flat, it may not be safe to decide that it *is* flat. There are problems to the flatness.

The first people who thought about the problems of the flat earth were certain Greeks who lived about twenty-five hundred years ago on what is now the western coast of the nation of Turkey.

One of them was a man named Anaximander. He wasn't satisfied with the tales of sun-gods and flaming chariots and flying horses. Instead, he looked at the night sky and asked himself what he really saw.

On a clear night, he saw the stars. During the night, they seemed to travel across the sky.

One star, however, didn't move. It was the North Star. It stayed in the same place in the northern sky all night long. It stayed there night after night. The stars near it moved in a circle around it. If the stars were very near it, they moved in small circles. If they were farther away, they moved in bigger circles.

The most important thing about the night sky to Anaximander was that the stars traveled in patterns. They weren't like a swarm of bees, in which each bee moves its own way.

The flat earth under the bowl of the sky.

The sun being rowed to the east during the night.

The sun god in his chariot by day.

The Indian belief.

The sphere of the sky around a central axis.

Instead, all the stars moved together.

Anaximander decided that the sky was a huge hollow ball, or "sphere." The sphere of the sky turned around on an invisible line or "axis." One end of the axis stuck through the sky where the North Star was situated. The other end was at the opposite side of the sphere where he couldn't see it.

Every day the sphere of the sky turned around, or "rotated." The stars were all stuck to the sky and turned with it. That's why they kept the same pattern. The sun and moon were stuck to the sky, too, and that's why they rose and set.

Even though the sky was a sphere, it was still possible for the earth to be flat. Anaximander thought it was a flat slab that stretched across the sphere of the sky at its center.

As the sphere of the sky turned, the sun rose in the east, traveled across the sky, and set in the west. The turning sky carried it along. Then as the sky kept turning, the sun was carried to the bottom part of the sphere. When the sun shone on the bottom side of the slab of the earth, it was night. When the turning sky carried the sun around to the east, it rose and it was day again. The moon and the stars also moved in this way. Anaximander's idea made more sense than the ideas of earlier thinkers. The sun was not destroyed each night nor was it rowed from west to east. Yet Anaximander wasn't satisfied. He kept on thinking.

THE DISAPPEARING STARS

If the earth were a flat slab that fitted tightly across the middle of the sphere of the sky, we could travel to the place where the earth and sky met. We could reach the place where the sun rose in the east and we could reach out and touch it (unless its heat killed us).

If we traveled far enough to the west, we could reach the place where the sun set.

Some people, centuries ago, really thought that could be done. They even drew pictures showing a man coming to the place where the sky touched the earth. The man could stick his head through the sky and see the machinery that kept the sphere of the sky turning.

The ancient Greek thinkers, however, didn't really believe that. After all, no matter how far to the east or west people traveled, they never seemed to get any closer to the sun, the moon, or the stars.

Perhaps, then, the earth didn't stretch from one side of the sky to the other. Perhaps our eyes only fooled us when they showed the sky touching the earth at the horizon.

Maybe the earth was a flat disc that was quite large but was far smaller than the sphere of the sky. If this were the case, the sun, the moon, and the stars would be far away from the edge of the earth. No one on earth would be able to reach them or even get particularly close to them.

But if the earth were a flat disc in the center of the sphere of the sky, with the sky far away on all sides, then why didn't travelers reach the end of the earth?

Perhaps because the land portion of the earth was in the middle of the flat disc and was surrounded by water. Travelers always reached the ocean if they traveled far enough. It was the ocean, then, that stretched out to the end of the earth. People, in ancient times, didn't travel far out of sight of the land. Maybe that was why they never came to the end of the earth.

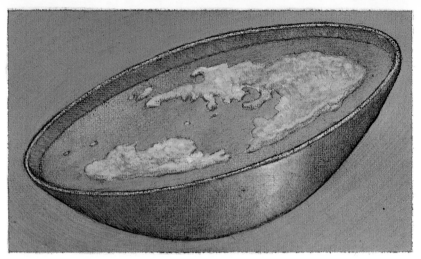

The earth as a shallow bowl.

But then why didn't the water of the ocean spill off the end of the earth?

Maybe the end of the earth was turned up at every side, so that the water was held in. Maybe the earth wasn't exactly a flat slab, but was a shallow bowl.

In that case, why didn't the whole earth simply fall?

It was still hard to consider the earth as flat, even if the sky was a huge sphere and the problem of sunrise and sunset was explained.

If the earth isn't flat, what other shape can it be?

Suppose we look at the sky again. In the sky, there are many shining objects, but most of them are stars. Stars are just little points of light to the eye and the ancient thinkers couldn't tell anything about them.

Two objects in the sky are different, however. They are the sun and the moon.

The sun is a circle of light at all times, but the moon isn't. Sometimes it *is* a circle of light, but sometimes it is only half a circle. Sometimes it is in between a whole circle and half a circle. Sometimes it is just a thin curve of light called a "crescent."

The Greeks who watched the moon, night after night, noticed that it changed its position in respect to the sun. They noticed that as it changed its position, it also changed its shape.

When the moon and sun were on opposite sides of the earth, the moon was always a full circle of light. The sun shone past the earth onto the moon. It lit up the whole side of the moon.

When the moon and sun were on the same side of the earth, they couldn't see the moon at all. The sun shone on the other side of the moon, the side they couldn't see. The side they could see received no sunlight and it was dark.

The ancient scholars who observed this decided the sun had light of its own and the moon didn't. The moon shone only because it was lit up by the sun. The moon shone by "reflected light."

The ancient Greeks had begun to work out the study of "geometry," which deals with the shapes of objects. They considered the different shapes of the lighted part of the moon. They considered the half-moons, the crescent-moons, and other types. They could easily show that in order for the lighted part of the moon to take on the shapes it did, the moon had to be a round ball, or sphere.

Then what about the shape of the sun? It shone on the moon and it did so equally well from all angles. Whether the moon and sun were on opposite sides of the earth, or on the same side, or anything in between, the moon received the same kind of light on the side that faced the sun. This could only have happened if the sun were a sphere.

With all this in mind, Anaximander could see that there were three objects in the sky that had a particular shape. There was the sun, the moon, and the whole sky itself. All three were spheres.

Did that mean the earth was also a sphere? Did that mean the earth was round instead of flat?

Not necessarily. Maybe the rules were different for the sky and earth. Just because the sky and a few objects in the sky were spheres didn't mean that the earth had to be a sphere. After all, the sun was hot and blazing but the earth wasn't. The moon moved through the sky, but the earth didn't seem to. The sky itself was full of stars but the earth wasn't.

No, in order to decide upon the shape of the earth, people had to consider the earth itself, and not other objects.

So let's go back to the earth and ask ourselves the following question: Would we see the stars differently from different parts of the earth?

We wouldn't if the earth were flat. Suppose we looked at the sky at night. We would see all the stars in the sky above us if the night were clear. If we were anywhere else on a flat earth, we would still see those same stars.

But that is not the way things really are!

There were many people, in ancient times, who had to travel. People who traveled north would notice that the sky at night seemed a little different. Some stars that they used to see near the southern horizon when they were at home couldn't be seen at all when they went northward. Then, when they returned home, those stars they hadn't been able to see showed up again just above the southern horizon.

People who traveled southward found things just the opposite. When they went south, they could make out stars just above the southern horizon that they never saw at home. When they returned, those stars disappeared again.

This was true of the northern horizon, too. At home, some stars dipped just a little below the northern horizon as they turned with the sky. If one traveled north, those stars stayed just a little above it. If one traveled south, stars that stayed a little above the northern horizon when one was at home began to dip below it.

The fact of the matter was that the stars were not seen from all parts of the earth, so the earth could not be flat.

The changing position of the stars.

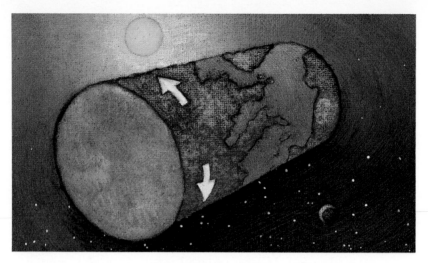

The earth as a cylinder.

Maybe the earth was shaped like a tin can, or "cylinder." This is exactly how Anaximander thought the earth might be shaped. He thought it was a cylinder lying in the center of the sphere of the sky. When you went north, you traveled along the curve of the cylinder. When you looked back, the curve hid some of the stars to the south. If you went south, you also traveled along the curve of the cylinder. When you looked back, the curve hid some of the stars to the north.

That explained the difference in the appearance of the sky as you went from place to place.

THE DISAPPEARING SHIPS

Anaximander's theory of a cylindrical earth raises some questions.

First, if the earth is cylindrical, why does it look flat?

That's not hard to answer. The earth is so large and we're so small that we can only see a tiny part of it as we look around.

The curve is so slight on a very tiny part of the earth that the surface looks flat.

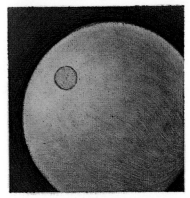

A tiny circle on a sphere looks flat.

To see this, imagine a large balloon blown up until it is a couple of feet across. Imagine a tiny circle on the balloon $1/8$ of an inch across. If a tiny insect could see only that much of the balloon, the surface of the balloon would appear flat.

Here is a second question that's harder to answer. If you are traveling down a curve when you go northward or southward, why don't you feel as though you are walking downhill? Why don't you start to slide?

You might think that the ground is so rough that it prevents you from sliding. But what if you're not traveling over rough ground? What if you travel by ship northward or southward over the smooth ocean? Why doesn't the ship start sliding forward? In fact, why doesn't the whole ocean just slide downward and all its water pour right off the earth?

Anaximander didn't have a good answer for that. He just felt that there was no other way to explain the appearance of the night sky than to suppose the earth had a cylindrical shape.

Why does the earth curve only if we go north and south? Suppose we go east and west. Does the appearance of the stars change? Do stars disappear behind the western horizon if we go east? Do they disappear behind the eastern horizon if we go west?

That's hard to tell. Since the sky turns, stars are always appearing at the eastern horizon and disappearing at the western horizon. Traveling east and west doesn't change that.

If the sky stopped rotating, it would be possible to tell whether stars were appearing and disappearing in the east and west. But the sky never stops rotating for even a moment, so that's no help.

But it's not very good to make a decision just because you have no evidence. To prove something, you need evidence.

Perhaps there's some other way of getting information about the shape of the earth, some way that doesn't involve the sky and the way it turns.

That kind of information can be obtained on the seashore and does not involve the sky.

If the earth were flat, a ship would get smaller and smaller as it sailed farther and farther away from shore. Finally, it would become a dot and disappear.

This, however, is not what happens. To begin with, someone watching a ship sail away can see the whole ship. He or she sees the wooden hull of the ship below and the sails above. After a while, however, the hull disappears. The water seems to reach above it and all that is left are the sails. Then only the top of the sails. Then the whole ship disappears.

Can it be that the ship is sinking? Is the water rising higher and higher, covering first the hull and then the sails?

That can't be, since it happens to every ship that sails away and most of them return safely. When a ship returned in ancient times, the sailors swore that at no time did the water rise above the hull.

How else could this be explained?

There was one way. Suppose the earth's surface curved. The ship would then sail away over that curve and would gradually

A ship disappearing over the horizon.

disappear behind it. Naturally, the bottom part would disappear first.

The ships were hidden by the curve of the earth, just as the stars near the horizon would disappear first.

But there was one great difference. You could see the stars disappear behind the curve of the earth only if you traveled north and south. In other directions, the turning of the sky spoiled things.

The ships, on the other hand, disappeared bottom-first, in *whatever* direction they went. They disappeared bottom-first, whether they went north, south, east, west, or any direction in between.

What's more, it always looked as though they disappeared at about the same rate. If they were two miles away, a certain amount of the hull was hidden, no matter in what direction they were sailing.

It looked as though the earth curved in *every* direction, and by the same amount in every direction.

But the *only* shape that curves by the same amount in every direction is a sphere. If you make a point on a large ball and draw a line away from that point in any direction, you will see that all the lines will curve in the same way.

Judging by what happens to ships, the earth is not a cylinder, but a sphere. It is a large sphere in the center of the much larger sphere of the sky. If the earth is a large sphere, then the tiny bit we can see at any one time looks flat.

A sphere curves equally
in all directions.

But that still leaves us with the question of why we don't slip off the earth when we move around and why the air and ocean don't slip off. Is there something else that can give us proof of the earth's shape? There is something, but for that we have to go back to the sky again.

THE EARTH'S SHADOW

Every once in a while, the moon loses its light. A black shadow moves across it until all one can see is a dim red glow. After a while, the shadow moves away and the moon is back again, shining as brightly as ever.

When this happens, the moon is said to be "eclipsed."

In ancient times, an eclipse of the moon frightened people. They thought the moon might remain dark forever and they did not want to lose the moon's helpful light at night.

Those who studied the sky carefully were sure this would not happen. They noticed, for instance, that an eclipse took place only at the time of the full moon. It never took place at any other time. What's more it only took place during certain full moons.

The ancient Greeks who studied the sky knew that when the moon was full, it was on the opposite side of the earth from the sun. The sun shone past the earth onto the moon. The sun lit up the entire side facing them and that is why the Greeks saw the moon as a full, round circle of light.

Suppose, however, that the earth was *exactly* in between the moon and sun. Then the sunlight would have to go through the earth to reach the moon. It couldn't do that, of course, so no light would reach the moon.

Another way of saying this is that the earth casts a shadow. During an eclipse, the earth's shadow falls on the moon and darkens it. Every once in a while, at the time of the full moon, the earth is exactly in between the moon and the sun, and at those times there is an eclipse.

When the earth casts a shadow on the moon, we can find out something about the shape of the earth. The first thing we notice is that the edge of its shadow is a curve that looks exactly like part of a circle.

The Greeks watched eclipses of the moon that took place in different parts of the sky. They watched eclipses when the moon was high in the sky, or low, or at the horizon. When the

The shadow of the earth on the moon.

moon was in different positions during an eclipse, the sun-light struck the earth from different angles. The shape of the shadow never changed. No matter where the moon was dur-ing the eclipse, the earth's shadow, as it moved across the moon, always looked like part of a circle.

This meant that the earth had a shape that cast a circular shadow in every possible direction. There is only one shape that does that, and that shape is a sphere.

About 450 B.C., a Greek scholar named Philolaus, who lived in southern Italy, was finally convinced.

He put all the evidence together. The change in the stars, the way in which ships disappeared as they moved away, and the shadow of the earth during an eclipse of the moon led him to one conclusion: The earth was a sphere located in the center of the much larger sphere of the sky.

So far as we know, Philolaus was the first man ever to say that the earth was a sphere.

But that still left questions. If the earth were a sphere and we were all living on top of it, why didn't we slide off as soon as we moved away from the top? Why didn't the ocean drip off and all the air drift away?

Let's think about this a little. Things fall downward. If we drop something, down it goes. But what do we mean by "down"? If the earth is a sphere and something falls down, it is falling toward the center of the earth.

This is true for every person on earth, no matter where he is standing. A person may be on one side of the sphere of the earth, or on the opposite side, or anywhere in between. Wherever he is, he and everything else about him are attract-ed to the center of the earth. Wherever he is standing, the center is always in the direction of his feet, so that his feet seem to be "down" and his head "up."

About 350 B.C., the Greek scholar Aristotle pointed this out clearly.

Aristotle's view that everything was attracted toward the center of the earth meant that the earth *had* to be a sphere.

This explains why the oceans and air stay on the spherical earth, and don't slide or drop off. Wherever they are, they are pulled "down" toward the center.

Down is toward the center of the earth.

MEET ISAAC ASIMOV, AUTHOR

While Isaac Asimov was growing up, he worked after school in his father's candy store. He was not allowed to read most of the magazines in the store, but because the magazine Science Wonder Stories *had the word* science *in the title, Asimov's father made an exception to his rule. When he was eighteen, Asimov had his first science-fiction story published in the magazine* Amazing Stories.

While working on advanced degrees in chemistry, Asimov continued writing stories. Later, when he worked as a teacher and researcher in biochemistry at Boston University, Asimov wrote a biochemistry book for students. He found that he enjoyed writing nonfiction even more than doing research. He continued to work as both a chemist and a writer until he decided to make his living as a full-time writer. Besides science fiction and nonfiction, Asimov wrote joke books, murder mysteries, explanations of history, and books about words, over four hundred books and a thousand articles in all. Astronomer Carl Sagan called him "the great explainer of the age." Asimov was a writer and a scientist who helped millions to understand the past, present, and future of our world and our universe.

THE
HEAVENLY ZOO
retold by Alison Lurie
illustrated by Monika Beisner

From the earliest times people have looked at the night sky and tried to understand what they saw there. Long before anyone knew that the stars were great burning globes of gas many millions of miles from the earth and from one another, men and women saw the sky as full of magical pictures outlined with points of light.

What shapes ancient people saw in the sky depended on who and where they were. Thus the group of stars that we call the Big Dipper, which is part of the Great Bear, was known to the Egyptians as the Car of Osiris, to the Norse as Odin's Wagon, and in Britain first as King Arthur's Chariot and later as the Plough. Many of the pictures that we see today are very old. The constellation we call the Great Dog was first known as a dog five thousand years ago in Sumeria; Taurus the Bull was already a bull in Babylon and Egypt.

Our ancestors saw all sorts of things in the stars: men and women, gods and demons, rivers and ships. But what they saw most often were beasts, birds, and fish. And for most of these creatures there was a legend of how they came to be there.

THE GREAT DOG

This story is from the Mahabharata, *which was written in India. Parts of this collection of stories were written more than two thousand years ago.*

Once upon a time in India there were five princes who left their kingdom to seek the kingdom of heaven. With them they took only food and drink for the journey; and the prince Yudistira brought his dog Svana.

Now besides Yudistira, who was the eldest, the brothers were Sahadeva the all-wise, who was learned beyond other men; Nakula the all-handsome, famed for his grace and beauty; Arjuna the all-powerful, who had never been defeated in any contest of arms; and Bhima the all-joyful, known far and wide for his good temper and love of pleasure.

So they set forth, and journeyed many days and many nights. Presently they came to a fair, where music was playing and people were drinking and dancing and feasting. Some of them saw Bhima the all-joyful, and called out for him to come and join them. Bhima said to himself, "I will rest here today and be happy, and seek the kingdom of heaven tomorrow." So he entered into the dance. And Yudistira and his brothers Sahadeva and Nakula and Arjuna and his dog Svana went on without him.

They traveled for many days and many nights, till they came to a broad plain where a great army was drawn up in ranks facing the enemy. When the soldiers saw Arjuna the all-powerful they shouted out, summoning him to come and lead them into battle. Arjuna said to himself, "I will fight today for my country, and seek the kingdom of heaven tomorrow." So he joined the soldiers; and Yudistira and his brothers Sahade-va and Nakula and his dog Svana went on without him.

So they traveled for many days and nights, till they came to a magnificent palace surrounded by a garden full of flowers and fountains; and in this garden a beautiful princess was walking with her attendants. When she saw Nakula the all-handsome she was seized with love and longing, and she cried out for him to come nearer. Nakula too was struck with love, and said to himself, "I will stay with this princess today, and seek the king-dom of heaven tomorrow." So he went into the garden, and Yudistira and his brother Sahadeva and his dog Svana went on without him.

They journeyed on for many weary days and nights, until they came to a great temple. When the holy men who lived there saw Sahadeva the all-wise they ran out, inviting him to come and join them in prayer and study. And Sahadeva said to himself, "I will stay here today, and seek the kingdom of heav-en tomorrow." So he went into the temple, and Yudistira and his dog Svana went on without him.

At last Yudistira came to Mount Meru, which is the door-way to heaven. And Indra the Lord of Past and Present appeared before him, and invited him to ascend. Yudistira bowed low and replied, "Very willingly I will do so, if I may bring my dog Svana with me."

"That may not be," said Indra. "There is no place in heaven for dogs. Cast off this beast, and enter into eternal happiness."

"I cannot do that," said Yudistira. "I do not wish for any hap-piness for which I must cast off so dear a companion."

"You traveled on without your four brothers," said Indra. "Why will you not ascend to heaven without this dog?"

"My lord," replied Yudistira, "my brothers left me to follow the desires of their hearts. But Svana has given his heart to me; rather than renounce him I must renounce heaven."

"You have spoken well," said Indra. "Come in, and bring your dog with you." So Yudistira and Svana ascended into paradise; and Indra, in recognition of their devotion to each other, set in the sky the constellation of the *Great Dog*, whose central star Sirius is the brightest of all in the heavens.

THE SCORPION

This story was told in ancient Greece.

Orion was one of the greatest of the Greek giants. Because he was the son of Poseidon, the god of the sea, he was as much at home in the water as on land. When he wished to get from one island to another he walked across on the bottom of the ocean; he was so tall that his head was always above the waves, and so large and broad that his travels caused high tides.

From childhood on Orion was famous for his beauty and his tremendous strength. He grew up to be a great hunter, able to track and slay all kinds of beasts with the help of his giant hound Sirius. When the island of Chios was oppressed and terrified by lions and wolves, Orion came to its assistance. He tracked down and destroyed every one, so that the people and their flocks could live in safety.

By the time Orion came to the large island of Crete, his fame was so great that Artemis, the goddess of the moon, invited him to go hunting with her. All went well until Orion, who had become vain of his skill, began to boast that he would soon have killed all the wild animals in Crete. Now the scorpion, who was listening, said to himself that this must not be. So he lay in wait for Orion, and stung him to death with his poisoned tail.

But Orion's spirit did not have to go down to dwell in the Underworld with the souls of ordinary mortals. The gods, who loved him, transported him instead to the sky, where he can be seen in his golden armor and sword-belt, holding up his golden shield, with his faithful dog Sirius at his heel. The scorpion who saved the wild animals of Crete was also raised into the heavens, and became a constellation in the southern sky.

Every night, as the *Scorpion* rises, Orion fades and vanishes.

CIRCLES, SQUARES, AND DAGGERS:
HOW NATIVE AMERICANS WATCHED THE SKIES
by Elsa Marston

You have probably heard about stargazers of the past such as the ancient Egyptians, the builders of Stonehenge, and the Mayas. Did you know that Native Americans, too, made astronomical observatories— long before Europeans arrived?

The study of these ancient observatories is called *archaeoastronomy*. By combining astronomy with archaeology, we are beginning to understand how people of the past observed the skies.

Archaeoastronomy is a very new field. The Native American observatories have been discovered—or their purposes understood—only recently. Most of the sites had been abandoned centuries ago, and their original uses had been forgotten.

Let's look at some of the different ways Native Americans devised to follow the movements of the sun and, in certain cases, the stars.

One of the most dramatic observatories lies on a windswept plateau high in the Bighorn Mountains of Wyoming. It is simply a circle of stones that looks something like a wheel, 80 feet across. In fact, it's called the Bighorn Medicine Wheel ("medicine" means holy or supernatural).

In the center of the wheel is a large pile of stones called a cairn. Twenty-eight lines of stones lead like spokes from the "hub" to the rim. Just outside the circle stand six smaller cairns.

Though the wheel had been known for about a hundred years, it was not until the early 1970s that its secrets began to come clear. An astronomer, John Eddy, discovered how the wheel "works."

The Bighorn Medicine Wheel. The diagram shows cairns marking sunrise and sunset on the summer solstice and the rising of the bright stars Aldebaran, Rigel, Sirius, and Fomalhaut.

© Dewey Vanderhoff

If you stand at a particular small cairn on the day of the summer solstice (usually June 21st), you will see the sun rise directly over the large cairn in the center of the wheel. At the end of the day, standing at a different pile, you'll see the setting sun line up with the center cairn. The medicine wheel tells almost exactly when the longest day of the year has arrived, the day we say summer begins.

The wheel shows other alignments as well. Pairs of small cairns were found to point to bright stars that shone briefly on the horizon on certain days before and after the summer solstice. These stars appeared roughly 28 days apart. Possibly the 28 "spokes" were supposed to help keep track of these intervals.

The Bighorn Medicine Wheel was probably built around 1700. The Ponca tribe claims that its ancestors constructed the original wheel. Other tribes probably added to it after moving into the area.

There is a similar medicine wheel in Saskatchewan, Canada. The Moose Mountain Medicine Wheel has cairns placed

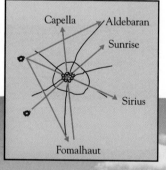

Fieldworkers at Moose Mountain. The diagram shows cairns marking sunrise on the summer solstice and the rising of the bright stars Capella, Aldebaran, Sirius, and Fomalhaut.

© Thomas F. Kehoe

like those of the Bighorn Wheel. This gave a clue to its age. The point on the horizon where a star rises changes slightly over time. The wheel was dated by figuring out when bright stars rose closest to the points shown by the cairns. The calculations agreed with carbon dating for the site. The Moose Mountain Medicine Wheel was probably built around 2000 years ago!

CIRCLES AND SQUARES

At Cahokia, a major Native American site in western Illinois near St. Louis, archaeologists discovered traces of four large circles of wooden posts. They reconstructed part of one of these circles.

Seen from the center at dawn, the sun lines up with certain posts at the summer solstice and winter solstice (the shortest day of the year, usually December 21st). A third post is aligned with the rising sun at the spring and fall equinoxes (usually

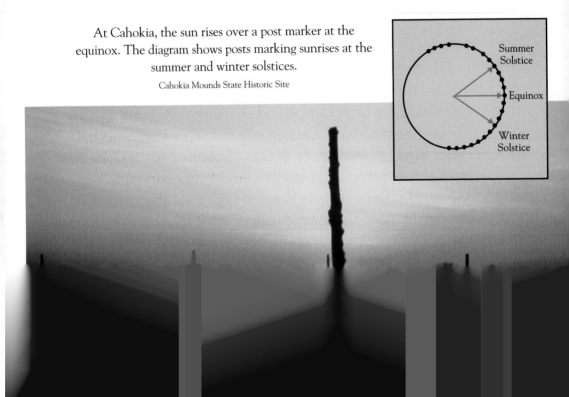

At Cahokia, the sun rises over a post marker at the equinox. The diagram shows posts marking sunrises at the summer and winter solstices.

Cahokia Mounds State Historic Site

March 21st and September 21st, when day and night are of equal length).

Another observatory was discovered near Kansas City, Missouri, in the early 1980s. Again, traces of posts were found, but this time in the shape of a square. About 35 feet long on each side, the square suggested a building such as a fort—except that the corners were open. A triangle of posts had stood in the center, and on the south side of the square was a double row of post marks.

A local astronomy society made a simple reconstruction of the square. They found that on the summer solstice, a person standing a certain distance from the center posts could see the sun rise and set through two of the open corners. The other two corners framed the sunrise and sunset at the winter solstice. On the equinoxes, the sun shone directly between the double lines of posts. Both observatories were made by Native Americans of the Mississippian culture, probably about a thousand years ago.

SUN DAGGERS

The Anasazi—a name that means simply "ancient ones"—lived in the beautiful but dry country of northern New Mexico, Colorado, Utah, and Arizona around 900 years ago. In Chaco Canyon, New Mexico, they designed an especially clever kind of observatory. It was discovered in 1977 by an artist, Anna Sofaer, who was examining rock carvings.

Near the top of Fajada Butte, a high rock that rises from the canyon floor, three large slabs of stone lean against a vertical rock face. About 9 feet long, they stand on end only a

Fall equinox.

Winter solstice.

Spring equinox.

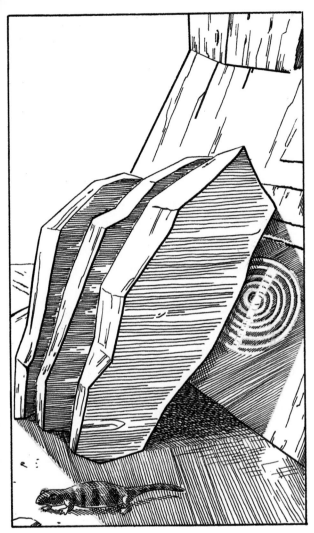

The solar marker in Chaco Canyon at noon
on the summer solstice.

few inches apart, their narrow sides against the rock. On the
shadowed rock behind them, two spirals have been cut.

At noon on the summer solstice, a tiny shaft of sunlight
falls between two of the slabs. It makes a spot that looks like a
dagger—cutting right through the middle of the larger spiral.

As the weeks pass, the "dagger" of sunlight moves to the right. Meanwhile, a second vertical streak of light appears. At the fall equinox, it cuts through the smaller spiral. By the winter solstice, the two "daggers" rest on the edges of the larger spiral. It's as though the spiral, now empty of sunlight, is a symbol of winter when the world is cold. Gradually, then, the sun daggers move to the left until, on the longest day of the year, the first one again strikes the center of the larger spiral.

All over the Southwest there are many such figures, called petroglyphs, cut in the rock. Spirals, crosses, rough outlines of humans, lizards, birds—all had meanings.

At many sites, the petroglyphs are touched by spots of sunlight, usually falling between two large rocks. Astronomer Robert Preston and his wife Ann, an artist, discovered many of these sites in Arizona. Light strikes the rock carving at the solstices, the equinoxes, or, in some cases, a point halfway between the fall equinox and the winter solstice.

"SUN ROOMS"

The Anasazi thought of other ways to observe the travels of the sun. Between Tucson and Phoenix, Arizona, rises a three-story adobe building known as Casa Grande ("Great House"). At dawn, a person standing inside this ancient structure will see the sun shining through a small hole high in the east wall. The spot of light strikes the opposite wall, moves toward a small hole in that wall, and disappears into it. The spot of sunlight hits this bull's-eye only on the days close to the spring and fall equinoxes.

Casa Grande a little after dawn, at the time of the spring equinox. Sunlight
passes through holes in two different walls, one behind the other.

© Jerry Jacka

There is a different type of Anasazi "sun room" at Hovenweep National Monument in Utah. Attached to a large stone
structure called Hovenweep Castle is a tower-like room. At
sunset on the solstices and equinoxes, the sun's rays enter
small holes and a door, shine through the room, and strike

Hovenweep Castle.
© Jerry Brody

doorways in the inside walls. The archaeoastronomer who studied Hovenweep Castle, Ray Williamson, determined that the beams of sunlight could not enter the room in this way merely by chance.

WHY?

All over this country, Native Americans came up with ingenious ways to observe the skies. But *why* did they study astronomy?

The skies were the Native Americans' calendar. They had no fixed, written calendar as we do today. They relied on what nature would tell them about the changing times of the year. Important solar events such as the solstices and the equinoxes helped them know when to plant their crops, when to start preparing for the winter, when to move from one place to another.

The sun and stars told Native Americans when important ceremonies were supposed to take place. These ceremonies were usually concerned with the "return" of the sun and start of a new year, and with planting, harvesting, and hunting.

Other special occasions might have been for social purposes such as tribal rituals, gatherings of tribes, trade, or payment of tribute. For example, the most likely function of the Bighorn Medicine Wheel was to keep a calendar so large groups could assemble in summer for trading fairs.

It's probable that only special persons knew how to use the observatories and make the announcements awaited by the people. The observatories must have strengthened the power of the chiefs and religious leaders.

There is a deep religious meaning in Native American astronomy. The sun is a vital symbol in the beliefs of many Native American cultures. And something equally important: Native Americans' understanding of the heavens helped them feel in harmony with the universe—for in many Native American religions, human beings are only one small part of the world, living in peace with the rest of nature.

Today we are coming to recognize Native Americans' achievements in astronomical knowledge—and to appreciate the ways in which they used that understanding.

SUN AND STAR CALENDARS

from SKY WATCHERS OF AGES PAST
by Malcolm E. Weiss
illustrated by David Rickman

*Using only the simplest of tools, ancient people kept track
of the movements of the sun, moon, and stars. This selection
describes sun calendars that were kept by the ancient Mayas
and star calendars that were kept by the ancient Egyptians.*

Where the horizon is hilly and uneven, it can be used as a sun calendar. A Native American group, the Hopi, use such a horizon calendar. Observing from the same place each day, the Hopi take note of where the sun rises and sets on important days. Each important day has the peak of a hill or the notch of a valley named after it—the peak or notch where the sun rises or sets on that day. The sun-watcher looks for the first glimpse of the sun in the morning, and for the sun's last gleam in the evening. He numbers the days with notches on a wooden stick, and warns the people when an important day is coming. The time for planting corn or beans, the time for the flute dance, the main harvest, and the winter-solstice ceremony—all are marked on the distant horizon.

Hopi horizon calendar showing sunsets from October 24 to December 21. Notice that on October 24, about the time for the Hopi corn harvest, the sun sets over a peak far to the right. By December 21, the time for the winter solstice ceremony, the sun sets over a peak far to the left. Ceremonies taking place near the end of winter were also marked by sunsets over peaks on the right. Ceremonies taking place in the summer were marked by sunsets over peaks even further to the right.

Halfway around the world, Russian peasants track the sun in the same way as the Hopi. In the Caucasus Mountains, village chiefs choose an old man to watch for sunset each day. He sits on a bench and watches the sun disappear behind the jagged mountain peaks. Using landmarks on the horizon to keep track of the year is a very old practice used by people everywhere.

This method could be used in early times because it was so simple. Nothing had to be built. All that was needed was a good view of the horizon, with natural landmarks and a place to stand while watching the sunrise and sunset.

But what if there is no clear view of the horizon? At Uaxactún, in the Mexican state of Yucatán, for example, the horizon is tree-covered and there are no landmarks to pinpoint the sun's position. There, in about A.D. 300, the Maya Indians used other means to measure the year. In a sense they built their own horizon, complete with landmarks.

Summer
Solstice

Spring or
Fall Equinox

Winter
Solstice

Mayan observatory at Uaxactún.

The Mayas developed a mighty civilization in Central America. Mayan civilization reached its peak between A.D. 100 and A.D. 900. Then, about a thousand years ago, the classic Mayan civilization collapsed. No one really knows why or how that happened.

At Uaxactún, the Mayas built a large pyramid. East of the pyramid, on a platform, they built three small temples. These temples were lined up with the pyramid, to fix the dates of the spring and fall equinoxes and the summer and winter solstices.

A priest stood on the steps of the pyramid, facing the middle temple. He sighted over the top of a stone column, to the center of the temple roof. At the equinoxes, the sun rose over the center of this roof.

Standing on the same spot at the time of the summer solstice, the priest could see the sun rise over the corner of the temple to his left—the northern temple. And at the winter solstice, the sun rose over the corner of the temple to the right—the southern temple.

Throughout their empire, the Mayas used similar means to plot the motions of the sun. And they did much more. They mapped the motions of the moon. They learned to predict eclipses of the sun and moon. They plotted the movements of the planet Venus with almost as much accuracy as do modern astronomers.

To do all this took careful observations over a period of several lifetimes. The Mayas had a written language that helped them pass along knowledge from one generation to the next. Most of that language is still a mystery to us. We have only decoded the signs for numbers and dates. These were the signs they used in making their calendars and astronomical tables. The signs included brilliantly colored pictures of gods, strange drawings of human and animal heads and skulls, and bars and dots.

These records were set down in "books" made of paper from the bark of the wild fig tree. A strip of paper making up a book was about eight inches high and several yards long.

Both sides were written on. The "pages" were separated from each other by painted lines. When the book was complete, the entire strip was folded up accordion-like along the lines that marked the pages.

These ancient picture books are now called codices. *Codices* is a Latin word, the plural of *codex*, meaning a book in manuscript form. Thousands of these codices were drawn and painted by the Mayas, and by the people of other Indian civilizations in Central America.

"Picture book" does not really do justice to the codices. Even the simplest-appearing pictures in the codices are more than pictures. They are words and often whole phrases or ideas in picture form. Simple symbols merge into not-so-simple ones, sometimes in a striking way. A wagging tongue, for example, means "talking." A wagging tongue surrounded by flowers means "singing."

Of the thousands of codices that once existed, only seventeen are left. The others were burned by the Spanish, who conquered the Mayan lands between 1519 and 1521. The high civilization of the Mayas had collapsed centuries before the Spanish arrived. But the descendants of the Mayas still lived according to the old traditions, and the ancient language was still spoken.

Many of the books were burned by Spanish soldiers. The remainder were destroyed by missionaries. Bishop Diego de Landa, of Merida, capital of the Spanish province of Yucatán, summed up the reasons for the burning: "We found a larger number of books . . . and as they contained nothing but superstitions and lies of the devil, we burned them all, which the Indians regretted to an amazing degree, and which caused them great anguish."

Yet Bishop de Landa knew that the books contained more than mere superstition. He wrote: "These people [the Mayas] also made use of certain characters or letters, with which they wrote in their books their ancient affairs and their science, and with these and drawings, and with certain signs in these drawings, they understood their affairs and made others understand them and taught them."

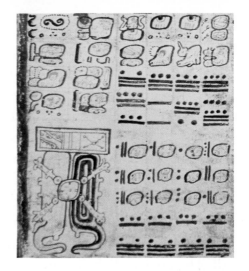

Eclipse tables from the
Dresden codex.

Sächsische Landesbibliothek
Dresden/Deutsche Fotothek

De Landa learned to speak the Mayan language. He discovered that large parts of certain codices were about astronomy and the Mayan calendar. In later years, he wrote down what he knew of the written language of the Mayas—largely how they wrote numbers and dates, and how they recorded national holidays, festivals, and astronomical events.

One reason the Mayas kept such careful count of days was that they believed the past foretold the future. As far as predicting the motions of the sun, moon, and planets is concerned, this is very nearly true. Their movements through the sky are repeated in regular cycles. Some of the cycles are simple; some are complicated. But by patient observing, Mayan astronomers found the patterns of many of these movements.

Some of the patterns are recorded in the Dresden Codex, which is now housed in a museum in Dresden, in Germany. The Dresden Codex is a collection of tables on the motions of the moon and the planet Venus. It is also a kind of horoscope, since the Mayas thought that the motions of heavenly bodies affected the fates of people on earth.

The Dresden Codex records the movements of Venus for over three hundred years. The Mayas calculated that the time it takes Venus to get back to the same point in the sky is 584 days. Using modern telescopes and observatory instruments, present-day astronomers have calculated the time as 583.92 days.

In the tables about the moon, the Mayas used the number 6585. As modern astronomers know, this is the period of time it takes for a series of eclipses of the sun and moon to repeat itself. The ancient Babylonians, who lived on the other side of the globe from the Mayas, also discovered and used this figure.

The Mayas did not use fractions or decimals, as the Babylonians did and as present-day astronomers do. They did learn to use whole numbers to express fractions very exactly, however.

For example, in the Dresden Codex the Mayas wrote that there are 405 moons (the time from new moon to new moon) in 11,958 days. If we divide 11,958 days by 405 moons, we get the length of one moon, or lunar month—29.52593 days. Modern astronomers use the figure of 29.5306 days.

In other words, the ancient astronomers of the Yucatán made an error of about seven minutes out of some twenty-nine days!

To keep watch on the stars, people invented what are probably the most ancient tools of astronomy—constellations, or sky pictures.

The constellations are star-finding tools. Most of us know that the pointer stars of the Big Dipper show the way to the North Star. We may recognize a few other easily seen sky groups such as Orion. Orion and the Big Dipper are bright enough to be visible even in the city, where skies are never completely dark. At best, not more than a few hundred stars are visible in city skies.

On a clear, moonless night in the country, far from city lights, you can see some three thousand stars, however. The bare outlines of familiar constellations are lost to us in the glow of unfamiliar stars. There is no shape or pattern to the thousands of sparkling points of light.

But if you look at the sky for a while, you will begin to see patterns and shapes. You will find yourself making up your own star pictures. This is what prehistoric peoples did from the earliest times.

In one group of stars, the Eskimos saw kayaks, and steps cut into the sides of a steep snowbank so hunters could climb to the top. In that same group of stars, the Egyptians saw a hippopotamus in the Nile River. The Blackfoot Indians of North America saw the arrowhead of a great hunter there. And the Cherokees saw three magicians. *We* know these stars as the Belt of Orion, the mighty hunter. That is how the ancient Greeks and Romans saw them.

Stories about the constellations were handed down by word of mouth for thousands of years. When people do not have a written language, such stories are more than entertainment. They are like star maps. They record where a constellation is in the sky, and what position it is in during each season. Early sky watchers found, as they had with the sun, regular patterns in the way the stars moved. This cycle of the stars, like the yearly cycle of the sun, allowed astronomers to measure the year.

Naturally, sky watchers could not fix the exact date when a star rose and set with the sun. For a good many days before

This detail of a calendar from the tomb of a pharaoh shows the months as Egyptian gods.

© Robert Lackenbach/Black Star

and after that date, the star would be invisible all night long. Its rising and setting would be hidden in the glare of sunrise and sunset.

But the ancient astronomers found a way around that difficulty. They watched for the *last* evening when a certain star was visible in the evening twilight. Then, some weeks later, they looked for the exact date when that same star was *first* visible in the east in the morning twilight. This first appearance of the star before dawn is the heliacal rising of the star. The ancient astronomers discovered that the amount of time between two *heliacal* risings of a star was one year. So the first heliacal rising of a particular star before dawn was often used by ancient people to mark important dates. Around the world, stars were used to mark times of the year for hunting, fishing, and planting; to mark the times of great cold or heat, the rainy season, and the dry season.

Some four thousand years ago, the Egyptians used the rising of Sirius—the brightest star in the sky—to mark the yearly flooding of the Nile River in July. This was the start of the Egyptians' calendar year. Their year had 365 days and 12 months. That was the amount of time the Egyptians counted between two heliacal risings of Sirius.

But as time passed, the Egyptians realized that something was wrong with their calendar. After only forty years, the heliacal rising of Sirius was ten days late, according to their calculations. After 730 years, it was half a year late. Not until 1460 years had passed were Sirius and the Egyptian calendar back in step. The Egyptians called this 1460-year cycle the *Sothic* cycle. Sothic was their name for Sirius.

The Egyptians realized that it was the calendar, not the star, that was out of step. If Sirius seemed late, this meant that the calendar year was shorter than the true year. So they began the practice of adding an extra day every four years. They passed this idea along to the Romans in the time of Julius Caesar. In 46 B.C., Caesar reformed the Roman calendar, adopting the Egyptian leap year.

That made the calendar $365\,1/4$ days long. This was quite accurate—just eleven minutes and four seconds longer than the true cycle of the seasons.

But it was still not accurate enough to keep the calendar in line with the seasons over very long periods of time. By 1582, the date of the spring equinox had slipped back to March 11. At that time, ten days were dropped from the calendar. The rules about leap years were changed, too. Only those century years—years ending in two zeroes—that were divisible by 400 would be leap years.

That meant that 1800 and 1900 were not leap years. But 2000 will be. The next century leap year after that will be 2400. With this correction, it will take the calendar 1,000 years to gain three days over the true year.

The reformed calendar of 1582 was proclaimed by Pope Gregory XIII, on the advice of the Jesuit astronomer Christopher Clavius. And neither Clavius nor the pope ever knew that more than eight hundred years earlier, Mayan astronomers had produced a calendar even more accurate than theirs.

GALILEO
from PIONEER ASTRONOMERS
by Navin Sullivan

Portrait of Galileo. Ottavio Leoni.
Date unknown.
Biblioteca Marucelliana. Photo: SCALA/Art Resource

One May evening in 1609, a carriage rattled briskly through the streets of Padua, in Italy. In it was Galileo Galilei, professor of mathematics, returning from a trip to Venice. While he was there, he had received news from a former pupil named Jacques Badovere—news that had sent him hurrying home.

"A marvelous tube is on sale here," wrote Badovere, who was now living in Paris. "This tube makes distant objects appear close. A man two miles away can be seen distinctly. People call these tubes 'Dutch perspectives' or 'Dutch cylinders.' Some say that they were invented by Hans Lippershey, an obscure maker of eyeglasses in Middleburg, Holland. What is sure is that they employ two lenses, one convex and the other concave."

The carriage turned into the Borgo dei Vignali and stopped outside Galileo's house. Pausing only to glance at his garden, Galileo hurried indoors and went to his study.

"One convex and one concave," he repeated as though in a trance. He drew writing paper toward him, dipped a sharpened quill in the ink, and began to draw.

"Suppose the convex lens is placed in front, to gather the light," he muttered. "Then if the concave lens is placed the right distance behind, it should magnify the gathered light."

He only had to figure the distance and he would be able to make one of these marvelous "Dutch perspectives" for himself! He had already taken the precaution of bringing a good assortment of eyeglass lenses from Venice.

By the time that Galileo went to bed he felt fairly sure that he had solved the problem. Early the next morning he hurried to his workshop. The place was filled with gadgets he had already invented, including an apparatus for indicating temperature and another for timing the pulse of a patient. Now he would make a tube to demolish distance.

Seizing a handy piece of lead tubing, he cut it down to the length he wanted. Then he took a convex lens and placed it in one end, and placed a concave lens in the other. Excitedly, he held the tube to his eye and peered through. Immediately he gave a cry of delight. It worked! The church tower several streets away might have been just outside.

How much did his tube magnify? Galileo cut different-sized circles of paper and pinned them up on a wall. When he found that his tube made a small circle look the size of a larger one seen with the naked eye, he could figure the magnification by comparing the actual sizes of the circles. In this

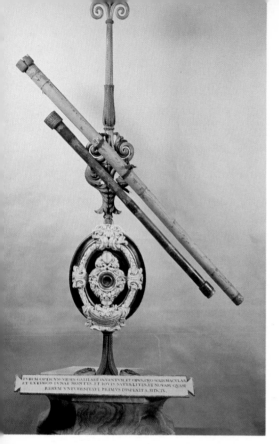

Two of Galileo's telescopes on display at a museum in Florence, Italy.

Museum of the History of Science, Florence.
Photo: SCALA/Art Resource

way he found that his telescope magnified three times.

Proudly he sat down and wrote to his friends in Venice telling them of his success. Then, after getting the lenses mounted in a more imposing tube made of wood, he hurried back to Venice himself. The Venetians were famous as sailors and navigators. This tube would show them ships out at sea long before they could be seen with the naked eye. Surely, thought Galileo, the nobles of Venice would pay well for such a device.

His thinking was right. On August 8, 1609, even the aged members of the Venetian Senate clambered painfully up to the very top of the tower of St. Mark's Cathedral, the highest building in Venice. There they gazed out to sea through Galileo's primitive telescope and, to their delight, found that they could see ships sailing toward them a good two hours before they were visible with the naked eye. They promptly doubled Galileo's salary as professor of mathematics which, although he was at the University of Padua, was controlled by them.

Galileo returned triumphantly to Padua and disappeared into his workshop. Already he was planning better lenses and longer tubes. He intended to teach himself lens grinding. He dreamed of magnifications of 8, 20, even 30!

And when he had made these telescopes, he was going to use them to look not at the sea but the sky. Five years earlier, all Padua had seen an extraordinary happening: a new star had appeared in the sky. (The astronomer Johannes Kepler had seen it too, and had pointed out that evidently the stars were not unchanging, as people then believed.) Like everyone else, Galileo had been surprised and puzzled by the new star. Now he promised himself that he was going to look more closely at the heavens.

It was four days after new moon. Galileo's newest telescope, magnifying 30 times, was resting in its cradle on a tripod stand. He squinted through it at the bright crescent, then drew what he saw by the light of a flickering candle.

The moon was, he knew, lit from one side by the sun. He noticed that the boundary between light and dark on the moon's surface was wavy and uneven. Also, he saw bright spots of light dotted over the dark area. What could they be?

He puzzled over them for a while, and then he made a bold deduction.

"These spots of light are mountain peaks just catching the sunlight," he decided. "And the wavy line at the boundary between light and dark exists because there are mountains there, too. It is sunrise up there and, just as on earth at dawn, the mountain peaks are bathed in sunlight while the valleys are still dark." It seemed incredible. Yet it must be true. There were mountains on the moon, as there were on earth!

Until then no one had seriously supposed that the moon might be something like the earth. People had thought of the moon and planets as heavenly bodies, things quite different in kind from the earth.

How high were the mountains? Galileo could not measure them directly, but he devised a way of comparing them with the diameter of the moon, which was fairly accurately known. When he had worked out the figures, he could hardly believe them. The moon mountains proved to be enormous, much higher than earthly mountains: up to four miles high.

It was a whole new world that Galileo was looking at. But was it full of living creatures or was it dead? He wondered if there was air on it, and shuddered at the idea that it might be cold and silent, a dead world forever circling the earth.

Then he began to explore the sky. Night after night he gazed upward, and what he found was a revelation. With the naked eye only about 2,000 stars are visible at any one time. Even with his relatively low-power telescope, Galileo found myriads more than that.

He examined the belt and sword of Orion: instead of the usual nine stars he found 89! The constellation of the Pleiades, in which sharp-eyed observers could only see seven stars, became a swarm of 43. As for the Milky Way— it was impossible to think of counting the stars in it. Wherever Galileo looked, his telescope showed crowded clusters of stars.

"Many of them are tolerably large and extremely bright," he noted, "but the number of small ones is quite beyond determination."

On January 7, 1610, while he was gazing at the sky an hour after sunset, he noticed that the planet Jupiter was visible. Immediately he turned his telescope onto it, eager to examine one of the planets for the first time.

He saw that it was a small, round disk that did not sparkle like a star. Peering more closely, he saw something else: three bright little points of light were grouped near it, two to the east of Jupiter, one to the west:

(East)   (West)

At first he told himself that these bright points must be three fixed stars. But the next night, to his astonishment, they were differently grouped: all three were to the west of Jupiter.

(East)   (West)

"Can Jupiter have moved past them?" Galileo asked himself in bewilderment. "If so, it is not traveling the way astronomers have always said it does."

He waited impatiently to look again the next night, but to his disappointment the sky was cloudy. However, the following night was clear. He rushed to his telescope and turned it with trembling hands toward Jupiter. This is what he saw:

(East)   (West)

For a moment he wondered if he were going crazy. Now there were only two points of light, and both were to the east of Jupiter.

"Is Jupiter moving back and forth like a pendulum?" he muttered.

He searched the sky nearby, checking to see if Jupiter had moved in this way against the background of the fixed stars. It had not; it was on the course that astronomers had always charted for it.

"If Jupiter is not swinging to and fro, then the little points of light are," reasoned Galileo. "And since one of them has disappeared tonight, it is probably hidden by Jupiter—it has probably gone behind the planet. It looks as if these points of light are swinging *around* Jupiter!"

This meant that the points of light could not be stars. To make sure that they were swinging around Jupiter, Galileo began a methodical series of observations.

On the next night, January 11th, he still saw only two of them, but now they had moved farther away from the planet. On the 12th they were closer again, and a third had appeared on the west of the planet. On the 13th, he had another surprise: there were four points of light.

(East) XOXXX (West)

He doubted no longer. "These are not fixed stars, but bodies belonging to Jupiter and going around it in various orbits," he decided. "Jupiter has four satellite moons of its own, just as the Earth has one!"

Full of excitement, he settled down to write a short account of all that he had discovered with his telescope. Two months later this was published in Venice, under the title *Messenger from the Stars*. His discoveries amazed the whole of Europe. Soon they were even being discussed in faraway Peking (now Beijing).

Galileo had opened up a new vision of the heavens. He had shown that the moon is a rocky, mountainous globe, that the earth is not unique in having a satellite moon, and that millions upon millions of stars exist. Soon he went further and discovered that Venus appears first as a crescent, then full, then dark, as it circles the sun and reflects light at different angles. He even traced the movement of mysterious spots across the face of the sun. The fact that the sun has spots shocked some people, who felt that a celestial object ought to be without blemish. Galileo, however, was very interested, for the movement of the spots, in one direction, indicated that the sun, like the earth, was spinning round on its axis.

To many people this probing of the skies was exciting. They realized that for the first time people had a means of exploring space. But to others it was unsettling, even dangerous. This was because, although they were living 70 years after Copernicus, they still believed that the earth did not move and was the center of the universe. The Church of Rome officially agreed with this belief, although some of its members did not.

Until now Galileo had not dared to defy the Church openly and declare that the earth moved round the sun.

"I would certainly dare to publish my ideas at once if more people like you existed," he had once written to Kepler. "Since they don't, I shall refrain from doing so."

However, his discoveries made Galileo a much more important man. He decided, finally, that the Church would not dare to curb him, and he began to state publicly that the earth circled the sun.

"Let them try to prove me wrong!" he exclaimed.

For some years the Roman Catholic Church let Galileo talk freely, only warning him from time to time, but many high officials of the Church remained unconvinced. And in fact, whatever Galileo said, he could not *prove* that the earth goes round the sun; he could only say, with Copernicus, that it seemed likely. (It was not until 1728 that conclusive proof was given by James Bradley, Third Astronomer Royal of England.)

In 1623 a new Pope was elected and the Church hardened against Galileo. He received more severe warnings than before, but would not give way. In 1632 he published a brilliant argument in favor of his beliefs, entitled *Dialogue on the Great World Systems*.

This was open defiance of the Church, and Galileo was summoned to appear before the Inquisition in Rome. Interrogation began on April 12, 1633. Galileo was asked to declare that he was wrong and that the earth stood still. The questioning continued for a month.

The great astronomer was now seventy years old, and he was worn out by fatigue and by fear of the Inquisition. In the end, Galileo did as he was told. Never again did he say in public that the earth moved.

Aristotle, Ptolemy, and Copernicus are shown on the cover of Galileo's book *Dialogue on the Great World Systems*.

The Bettmann Archive

TELESCOPES
from THE WAY THINGS WORK
by David Macaulay

TELESCOPES

A telescope gives a close-up view of a distant object, which, in the case of an astronomical telescope viewing a far-off planet or galaxy, is very distant indeed. Most telescopes work in the same basic way, which is to produce a real image of the object inside the telescope tube. The eyepiece lens then views this image in the same way as a magnifying glass. The viewer looks at a very close real image, which therefore appears large. The degree of magnification depends mainly on the power of the eyepiece lens.

REFRACTING TELESCOPE

In a refracting telescope, an objective lens forms the real image that is viewed by the eyepiece lens. The image is upside down, but this is not important in astronomy.

REFLECTING TELESCOPE

In a reflecting telescope, a large concave primary mirror forms the real image that is then viewed by an eyepiece lens. Usually, a secondary mirror reflects the rays from the primary mirror so that the real image forms beneath the mirror or to the side. This is more convenient for viewing.

Reflecting telescopes are important in astronomy because the primary mirror can be very wide. This enables it to collect a lot of light, making faint objects visible. Collecting light from an object is often more important than magnifying it because distant stars do not appear bigger even when magnified.

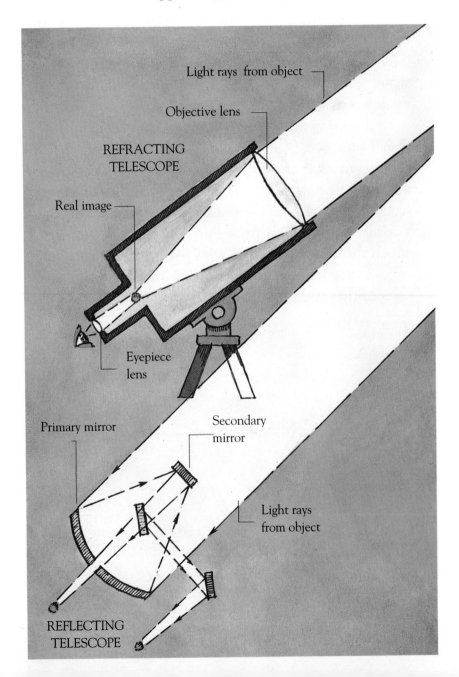

Light rays from object

Objective lens

REFRACTING
TELESCOPE

Real image

Eyepiece
lens

Primary mirror

Secondary
mirror

Light rays
from object

REFLECTING
TELESCOPE

Many objects in the universe send out radio waves, and a radio telescope can be used to detect them. A large curved metal dish collects the radio waves and reflects them to a focus point above the center of the dish, rather as the curved mirror of a reflecting telescope gathers light waves from space. At this point, an antenna intercepts the radio waves and turns them into a weak electric signal. The signal goes to a computer. Radio telescopes detect very weak waves, and can also communicate with spacecraft.

By detecting radio waves coming from galaxies and other objects in space, radio telescopes have discovered the existence of many previously unknown bodies. It is possible to make visible images of radio sources by scanning the telescope or a group of telescopes across the source. This yields a sequence of signals from different parts of the source, which the computer can process to form an image. Differences in frequency of the signals give information about the composition and motion of the radio source.

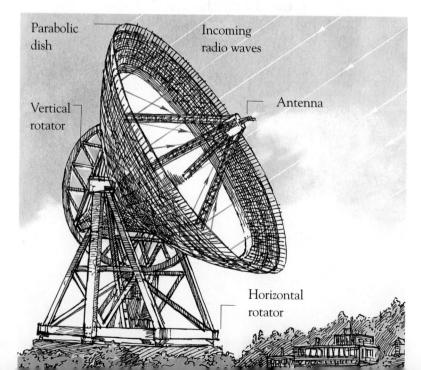

Parabolic dish

Incoming radio waves

Vertical rotator

Antenna

Horizontal rotator

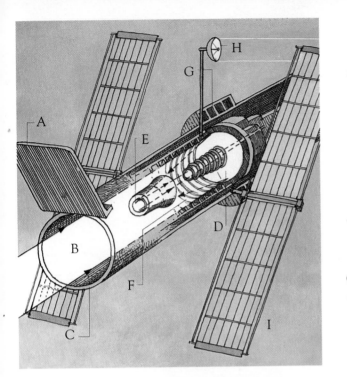

SPACE TELESCOPE

A. Aperture door

B. Light rays from star or galaxy

C. Telescope tube. The main body of the telescope is 43 feet long and 14 feet across.

D. Primary mirror. The space telescope is a reflecting telescope with a main mirror 8 feet in diameter.

E. Secondary mirror

F. Baffles. These ridges reduce the reflection of stray light from surfaces in the tube.

G. Equipment section. Light detectors change the visual images produced by the mirrors into television signals. The space telescope also contains scientific instruments.

H. Radio dish. The dish sends telescope images and measurements from instruments back by radio to ground stations below.

I. Solar panels. The pair of panels provides electricity to work the instruments aboard the space telescope.

The Hubble space telescope is part optical telescope and part satellite. It promises to revolutionize astronomy because it operates outside the atmosphere, which hampers any observations made from the ground. The space telescope orbits the earth, observing distant stars and galaxies in the total clarity of space. It can peer seven times further into the universe than we can see from the ground, and can also detect very faint objects. The telescope may be able to "see" far back in time by observing ancient light waves from the most distant galaxies. Among these may be light waves produced just after the big bang that blew the universe into existence some 15 billion years ago.

FINE ART
ASTRONOMY

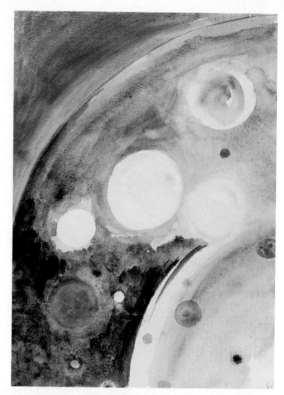

Cosmic Universe. c. 1957.
Natalia Goncharova.

Watercolor on paper. Gift of Wallace and
Wilhelmina Holladay, The National Museum of
Women in the Arts, Washington, D.C.

The Starry Night. 1889.
Vincent van Gogh.

Oil on canvas, 73.7 cm x 92.1 cm.
Acquired through the Lillie P.
Bliss Bequest, The Museum of
Modern Art, New York

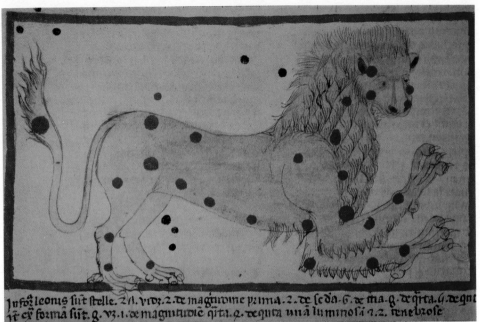

The constellation of Leo. c. 1500.

Ink and paint on vellum. The British Library, London. MSS 23770 13v. Photo: Bridgeman Art Library/SuperStock

Astronomers working in an Istanbul
observatory. 16th century.

Turkish miniature. Istanbul University Library.
Photo: R. & S. Michaud/Woodfin Camp & Associates

Tycho Brahe pictured at Uranienborg, a castle and
observatory he built on the island of Hven. From
Astronomiae instauratae Mechanica, 1602.

Copper engraving. Photo: The Bettmann Archive

VOYAGER TO
THE PLANETS
from the book by Necia H. Apfel

❧ 182 ❧

Voyagers 1 and 2 are space probes, spacecraft sent to explore other planets. Space probes carry instruments that collect information and send photographs and other data back to earth.

Before the Voyagers, space probes had been sent to gather information from Mars, Venus, Jupiter, Saturn, and Mercury. Voyager 1 flew by Jupiter and Saturn. Voyager 2, however, was the first space probe to go on a "grand tour" of several planets. This selection follows the long journey of Voyager 2 from the time it left Earth.

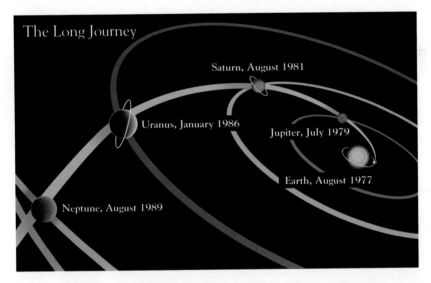

Diagram of Voyager 2's twelve-year journey to Jupiter, Saturn, Uranus, and Neptune.

On August 20, 1977, Voyager 2 was placed atop a Titan 3-E/Centaur rocket at the United States launching site on Cape Canaveral in Florida. The rocket blasted off and rose majestically into the clear blue sky.

All was well. But now the real countdown began. Voyager would take two years to reach its first destination—the giant planet Jupiter.

Voyager is a strange-looking machine with tubes and box-like structures sticking out all over it. These contain its many instruments, including cameras, radio receivers, and ultra-violet and infrared sensors. The instruments were designed to collect data from places Voyager would visit and to send this information back to Earth, where scientists and engineers were eagerly awaiting the reports.

Sometimes instructions had to be sent from stations on Earth to Voyager, telling it when to change its position, what data to record, or which instruments to use. Voyager was equipped with a big umbrella-shaped antenna to receive these directions.

In designing Voyager, the engineers tried very hard to anticipate any problems or emergencies that might arise on its

The Voyager spacecraft.
Jet Propulsion Laboratory

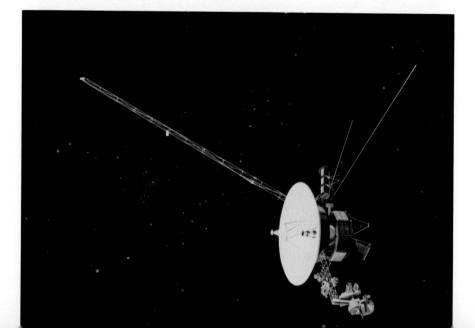

long journey. But the first difficulty occurred much sooner than they expected. Only eight months after Voyager was launched, its primary radio system stopped working and the backup radio receiver developed a short circuit. These defects drastically reduced Voyager's ability to receive instructions from the scientists. New computer programs had to be sent to Voyager so that it could respond to future commands. The scientists could only hope that the defective radio system would last for the entire journey. Otherwise, there would be no way for them to communicate with Voyager.

With its faulty radio operating weakly, Voyager kept sailing farther into space. After two years it finally arrived at the colorfully banded planet Jupiter, passing closest to it on July 9, 1979.

Jupiter is so big that more than 1,300 Earths could fit inside of it. It has more material in it than all the other planets in the solar system combined. It is truly a giant planet.

Following commands from programmers on Earth, Voyager took pictures of Jupiter's clouds, recorded their temperatures and speeds, and analyzed their composition. The spacecraft found that it is very cold out there, a half-billion miles from the sun. Jupiter receives only one twenty-fifth the sunlight we receive on Earth. Its pretty clouds have temperatures of about -230° F. Deep inside Jupiter it is much warmer, and at the planet's center the temperature rises to 54,000° F. That's around five times as hot as the surface of the sun.

This great heat rising from the interior would make Jupiter's cloud tops look like a multicolored bubbling mixture if the planet were not turning around rapidly on its axis. But Jupiter rotates very fast. A day on Jupiter lasts only ten hours.

The planet Jupiter. The Great Red Spot is just below the planet's equator.
NASA

This rapid rotation causes the clouds to be pulled out into a series of colored bands. Different substances in the clouds give them their varied colors.

The bands of clouds circling Jupiter are not smooth or featureless. Within them are huge, turbulent storms, whirlpools, and other disturbances. Weather on this giant planet is extremely violent and forceful. The most noticeable storm is called the Great Red Spot. It is so big that it can be observed through telescopes on Earth and has been seen for at least three hundred years.

Long before Voyager was launched, astronomers knew that the Great Red Spot was a giant storm, towering 10 miles above the rest of the clouds that swirl around it. Through their telescopes, they had seen the Red Spot change in size and in brightness, although it never seemed to vanish completely. Voyager's pictures showed the Red Spot to be about the size of Earth, but at other times it was known to be three times the size of Earth. Its color also varied from bright cherry

A closeup of the Great Red Spot surrounded by turbulent cloud formations.
NASA

ry red to very faint reddish hues. Astronomers aren't sure why the Great Red Spot appears red or why it has lasted such a long time.

Although the Great Red Spot drifts around the planet, it is always about the same distance below Jupiter's equator. As it drifts, it also rotates, taking about six days to turn around once. This rotation and drifting cause the gases around the Red Spot to eddy and swirl, somewhat like the way rocks and other barriers cause a rapidly rushing stream of water to froth and foam into small whirlpools and eddies. The photographs taken by Voyager show these eddies and swirls in great detail.

Jupiter is the center of its own miniature solar system. It has at least sixteen moons, three of which were discovered by Voyager. Four of Jupiter's moons are very large, with diameters of several thousands of miles. The other twelve moons are no bigger than a few hundred miles across, and many are much smaller.

We now know that all four of the planets visited by Voyager have ring systems. Saturn's magnificent ring system was discovered about 1610 by Galileo. In 1977, more than 350 years later, faint rings around the planet Uranus were detected through powerful telescopes. Astronomers started theorizing that perhaps Jupiter and Neptune also had ring systems. Voyager proved them right when it discovered rings around both planets.

From afar, all these ring systems appear solid, but they are actually composed of thousands of individual chunks of ice, all following similar orbits around a planet. Saturn's rings are the most spectacular, but all four ring systems are fascinating in different ways.

Voyager found that Jupiter's ring system is just a single ring consisting of several parts with no gaps between them. The brightest part is the outer edge, but even this section is too faint to be detected from Earth. Just outside this edge Voyager found two very small moons. Both moons race rapidly around Jupiter, taking only about seven hours to complete their orbits. By contrast, our moon takes twenty-nine and one-half days to orbit Earth, which is a much smaller planet.

By moving so quickly, these tiny moons prevent any ring particles from straying beyond the ring's outer edge, farther out into space. Astronomers call such moons shepherd satellites because, like sheep dogs with sheep, they keep ring particles confined within certain regions.

Because no shepherd satellites control the inner particles of Jupiter's ring system, they have spread out very thinly, reaching all the way to Jupiter's cloud tops. Only when Voyager was very close to Jupiter could it detect this faint, wispy diffusion of tiny particles.

L eaving Jupiter, Voyager headed farther into the frigid emptiness of space. For two more years it traveled outward another half-billion miles, reaching the ringed planet Saturn in August 1981.

Saturn's rapid rotation, like Jupiter's, causes its clouds to appear as colorful bands. But Saturn has no giant storms like Jupiter's Great Red Spot. It has much smaller storms that look brown and white in Voyager's photographs.

Saturn also has much less material in it than Jupiter. In fact, although it is the second largest planet and has a diameter ten times that of Earth, it is a lightweight planet. Saturn is so light that it would actually float on water if it were put into a swimming pool large enough to hold it.

The planet Saturn.

Jet Propulsion Laboratory

The many rings of Saturn. Differences in the color of the rings indicate different chemical compositions.

Jet Propulsion Laboratory

A thick layer of haze covers Saturn, making its atmospheric markings look much more muted than Jupiter's. Its clouds appear in different shades of butterscotch rather than bright orange, yellow, and white.

Nothing obscures Saturn's magnificent rings. Billions of icy particles orbit the planet in a flat sheet, extending outward more than 45,000 miles. But the thickness of this sheet is only about one hundred yards, the length of a football field. The rings cast shadows on Saturn's clouds but are thin enough for stars to be seen through them, even from Earth. As Voyager had found at Jupiter, shepherd satellites help herd the tiny particles of Saturn's rings into confined orbits.

Saturn, like Jupiter, has its own solar system, with at least eighteen moons. But Saturn has only one large moon, Titan. The rest are quite small. Eight of these have been called "moonlets" or "the Rocks" because they are very tiny, irregular chunks of rocky material. Some of them are shepherd satellites.

Titan, on the other hand, is bigger than the planet Mercury. It is also the only moon in the solar system that has a thick atmosphere. This atmosphere is so thick, in fact, that Voyager couldn't see Titan's surface at all. Titan's atmosphere is mainly nitrogen, much like Earth's atmosphere, which also contains oxygen. Titan lacks oxygen, the element so vital to life on Earth.

Beneath its thick, smoglike clouds, Titan's surface must be a dark, gloomy place, much like the depths of an ocean on Earth. Because of its nitrogen atmosphere, Titan may be the way Earth was billions of years ago. Of course, Titan is much colder than Earth ever was. Its surface temperature is around –296° F.

Voyager had been carefully aimed so that Saturn could give it a gravity-assist change of direction toward Uranus. Before Voyager 2 reached Uranus, however, the engineers found that the spacecraft had lost much of the lubricant needed to keep its scanning platform operating. Without the ability to turn easily, the cameras mounted on this platform could not be aimed properly. Instead, the entire spacecraft would have to be rotated, a much more difficult maneuver. Also, Voyager's computer software, especially those commands controlling Voyager's stabilization and photographing instructions, had to be redesigned.

The engineers knew that whereas Voyager had been able to spend several days at Jupiter and Saturn, it would have only about six hours at Uranus. And because Uranus is so much farther from the sun than either Jupiter or Saturn, much, much less sunlight reaches it. Taking a picture at Uranus has been compared to photographing a ball park at night by the light of a single candle.

The engineers calculated that Voyager would be moving at about 12 miles per second when it went past Uranus. This meant that in 10 seconds it would move 120 miles. So Voyager's camera had to be moved backward at just the right speed to compensate for this rapid forward motion. All these commands had to be sent to Voyager almost three hours beforehand, because that's how long it takes light or radio waves, traveling at the speed of light, to reach the planet from Earth.

Also, because of the increased distance, Voyager's radio signals back to Earth became much weaker. The engineers had to expand the Deep Space Network that tracked and communicated with Voyager. To do this, they started using powerful radio telescopes, such as the Very Large Array (VLA) in New Mexico and a similar one in Australia. These large series of connected radio telescopes act as one huge telescope, detecting radio waves too faint for a single receiver to pick up. Once again, when Voyager had in effect radioed home for help, the engineers were able to devise new and brilliant solutions. Voyager's engineers were the real heroes of this story.

All these preparations took place while Voyager silently traveled onward. On January 24, 1986, after four and a half long years, the sturdy spacecraft came within about 50,000 miles of Uranus. It was only 10 miles off the desired point after having traveled 2 billion miles from Earth.

Uranus was discovered during the time of the American Revolutionary War. In 1781, the English astronomer Sir William Herschel realized that what previously had been recorded as a star was actually the seventh planet in our solar system. Many years later, five moons were found orbiting Uranus, and then in 1977 Uranus's ring system was detected.

Uranus's main peculiarity, however, was known long before Voyager's journey. It is not the planet's rings or its moons that are unique. It is the planet itself. Unlike other planets, which rotate in an upright position, Uranus rolls along in its orbit like a top spinning on its side. As a result, during half of its eighty-four-year orbit Uranus's north pole faces the sun, and during the other half its south pole is sunlit. Uranus's moons and rings also follow this strange orientation because they all have orbits directly above Uranus's equator.

Astronomers were disappointed at how few features Voyager was able to detect in Uranus's clouds. Layers of thick haze hang over most of the upper clouds, obscuring any details that may exist below. A small amount of methane gas in the haze and clouds gives the planet its soft blue-green color.

Although Voyager found Uranus almost featureless, the visit was not in vain. Besides discovering ten new Uranian

The planet Uranus. One of Uranus's moons, Miranda,
is shown in the foreground.

NASA

moons and obtaining close-up photographs of the five known ones, Voyager was able to distinguish ten very narrow rings of particles in Uranus's ring system. The rings are widely separated by several shepherd satellites that were among the ten new moons found by Voyager.

Particles in the rings are made of ice but are covered with sootlike material, which makes them appear very dark. Most of the particles are about the size of a fist or bigger. One would expect to find smaller particles as well, possibly as small as dust. Astronomers theorize that some process must be sweeping the rings clear, leaving only the larger chunks.

The astronomers would have liked Voyager to linger longer at Uranus. But even as the spacecraft approached Uranus, they were preparing speed and direction commands to be radioed to it. With a gravity-assist from Uranus, Voyager would head toward Neptune.

By the time Voyager arrived at Neptune, the engineers were already jokingly describing the spacecraft as being hard of hearing with a touch of arthritis and a slight loss of memory. Voyager was a very old spacecraft indeed.

However, Voyager came closer to Neptune than it did to any other object in its long journey. It passed 2,700 miles above the cloud tops over Neptune's north pole. That was on August 25, 1989, twelve years after its launch. Voyager was now 2 3/4 billion miles from Earth. The spacecraft was so far from the people who sent commands to it that it would have to operate at the very limit of its capability to hear their directions.

Neptune is too far away from us to be seen without a telescope. Sunlight reaching Uranus is very dim, but it is two and a half times as much as the amount of light reaching Neptune.

Neptune receives only one-thousandth the amount of light we receive on Earth.

Astronomers thought that Neptune would be featureless like Uranus. They were delightfully surprised. Neptune is about the same size as Uranus and shares the same blue-green color because of a small amount of methane in its clouds. But heat rising from Neptune's hot interior keeps its cloud top temperatures similar to Uranus's temperatures, even though Neptune is more than a billion miles farther away from the sun.

This rising heat drives fierce winds, creating huge storms in Neptune's atmosphere, much like those found on Jupiter. Instead of finding a peaceful-looking planet, Voyager found active cloud structures in a turbulent state.

The planet Neptune. The Great Dark Spot is at the equator, just above the white cloud.

NASA

Neptune's biggest feature is called the Great Dark Spot, which is a huge rotating storm about the size of Earth. Unlike Jupiter's Great Red Spot, the Great Dark Spot is a hole or depression in the clouds. It lets us look deep into Neptune's atmosphere, although all we see is darker shades of Neptune's blue-green methane covering.

About 30 miles above the atmosphere, white cirruslike clouds form and dissipate around the Great Dark Spot, similar to the way clouds form on mountainsides on Earth. White wispy clouds are also found near a small triangular-shaped storm, which moves around the planet faster than the Great Dark Spot and has therefore been dubbed Scooter. Another storm, Dark Spot Two, is smaller than the Great Dark Spot and is oval in shape. It has a white cloud hovering above its center.

The thick blue-green clouds covering Uranus and Neptune make up only about 10 to 20 percent of the planets' mass. The rest is rock and ice beneath the clouds. Uranus and Neptune are not true gas planets like Jupiter and Saturn. Scientists believe that they may be the accumulation of thousands of huge boulders that crashed together and formed planets early in the solar system's history.

After Voyager confirmed that both Jupiter and Uranus had ring systems, astronomers were fairly sure that Neptune would have one, too. They were, therefore, not surprised when Voyager detected it. When the spacecraft was still far away from Neptune, the pictures it sent back to Earth showed only sections of rings. Not until Voyager was much closer could the rest of the rings be observed. The brighter sections seen at first were found simply to have more material in them, making them more visible. And once again, Voyager detected shepherd satellites confining two of the first three rings it discovered into very narrow areas. The third ring is much more spread out. Later, after studying Voyager's photographs more closely, astronomers discovered a fourth and fifth ring.

Voyager also found six new moons orbiting Neptune, raising the total number known to eight. But most amazing was what Voyager discovered about Triton, Neptune's largest moon. Although Triton had been observed from Earth many years before, little was known about it other than that it was one of the largest satellites in the solar system. Triton orbits Neptune in a retrograde motion, which means that it goes

A portion of Neptune's largest moon, Triton.
Seasonal changes cause melting and collapsing of its icy surface. *Inset:* A detail of Triton's south pole shows what may be ice volcanoes.

NASA

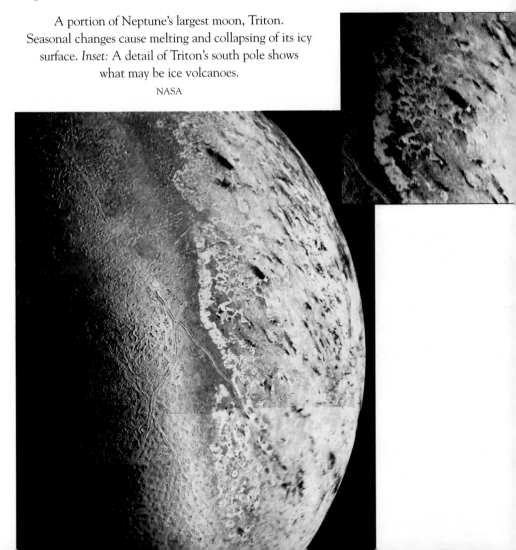

around Neptune in the direction opposite to Neptune's spin. It is the only major moon in the solar system to have this characteristic, although some of the smaller moons of Jupiter have retrograde motion.

The surface of Triton, as revealed by Voyager, is fascinating. Bright snowfalls only a few decades old contrast with craters billions of years old. In general, however, craters are very scarce on Triton, indicating that its crust is quite young and is constantly changing.

Voyager found several active volcanoes on Triton. The material coming from them is not molten rock like the hot lava that comes out of volcanoes on Earth. Instead, water mixed with other substances is spewed out, making the volcanoes more like geysers.

Voyager also photographed dark plumes of dust-filled nitrogen gas erupting from beneath Triton's surface. The gas rises some 5 miles into the thin atmosphere before being blown more than 150 miles across the moon. The dark plumes are seen as streaks of black on the much lighter landscape.

After Voyager 2 passed Neptune, its program was given a new name—Voyager Interstellar Mission (VIM)—because now it is headed out of the solar system, out to the stars.

Very little will change on Voyager as it sails on through outer space. Eventually its electrical power will be used up and its instruments will cease to function, but there is nothing in space that will stop Voyager from traveling

One of Voyager's last pictures of
Neptune and Triton.

NASA

farther and farther from us. Only when it comes close enough to be affected by another star's gravitational attraction will its path be altered. Astronomers have calculated that that won't happen for at least twenty-seven thousand years!

We don't know if there are any intelligent beings elsewhere in the universe, but if there are—and if they find either of the two Voyagers wandering out in space—they will discover, in addition to all the instruments, a very special gold-plated record on the side of each spacecraft. On each record is a recorded greeting from the people on Earth in fifty-five languages as well as many sounds that are common on Earth. These include the roar of a jet plane, the crying of babies, the chirping of crickets, and ninety minutes of a variety of music. Covering this precious record is a diagram showing what Earth people look like and where Earth is in the solar system. The story of Voyager will be an ancient legend before any alien being can possibly find the spacecraft. But maybe, many thousands of years from now . . .

MEET NECIA APFEL, AUTHOR

Necia Apfel's childhood interest in astronomy was discouraged. "Women don't become astronomers," she was told. Her interest was renewed when her husband gave her a telescope for her birthday, and she began graduate study of astronomy at Northwestern University. As a graduate research assistant, she coauthored a college textbook on astronomy. Since that time she has written several books for children and teenagers about astronomy. She has also lectured for children at the Adler Planetarium in Chicago and written a monthly column in Odyssey magazine answering readers' questions about astronomy. "Only children can think up the kinds of questions I receive," she said. "They are marvelous."

A MEETING IN SPACE

from BARBARY by Vonda N. McIntyre
*illustrated by Mary Beth Schwark
and Bob Kuester*

*Orphaned Barbary and her cat Mick have come to the space
research station Atlantis to live with her mother's old friend
Yoshi and his daughter Heather, who has a serious heart
condition. Barbary arrives at an exciting time. An alien
spacecraft has entered Earth's solar system. Yoshi's friend Thea,
an astronomer, plans to send a probe with a camera to learn
more about the alien craft. But when the probe is launched,
Barbary finds that Mick is aboard it. In trying to rescue him she
herself will play a role in the first meeting between the
aliens and Earth people.*

B arbary entered the launch chamber. Heather's raft sat
on its tracks, waiting to go out again. Barbary floated to
it, opened its door, and slid into the seat.

She stared at the controls. She thought she remembered
what Heather had done, but she was not certain. She was not

even sure she could figure out in which direction to go to find the alien ship, and Mick's raft. Away from the sun, she guessed. But there was an awful lot of nothing out there, and rafts were awfully small.

Heather said the computer could drive the raft —

She turned it on.

"Can you hear me?"

"I can hear you."

"Do you know where the raft with the transmitter is?"

"Yes."

"I want to go there."

"Please wait."

The kaleidoscope patterns appeared. Barbary gritted her teeth. Computers were supposed to know everything instantly.

But if it knew the location of Mick's raft, why was it making her wait? The only reason she could think of was that it was reporting her.

She slapped the switch that turned off the computer. She did not know if that would keep it from reporting her—if that was what it was doing—but it was the only thing she could think of. She would have to find Mick herself. She pulled down the door and sealed it and tried to remember what control Heather had used first.

"Open up!"

Barbary started at the muffled voice and the rap on the transparent roof.

Heather stared in at her. She looked furious.

Barbary opened the hatch.

"Move over!"

"Heather, they're going to shoot Thea's contraption, and Mick's inside it. I have to stop them—"

"Move over!"

Barbary obeyed.

Heather swung in, slammed the hatch shut, and fastened her seat belt.

"Your computer told me part of it, and I figured out the rest." She took over the controls.

"Thea tried to make her camera come back, but it wouldn't."

"Mick probably knocked loose some of the connections."

Their raft slid into the airlock. The hatch closed.

"I just hope I got here soon enough to get us out," Heather said. "I bet they'll freeze all the hatches in about two seconds, if they haven't already—"

The outer door slid open.

Heather made a sound of triumph and slammed on the power. The acceleration pushed them both back into their seats.

With the raft accelerating and the station growing smaller behind them, Heather glared at Barbary.

"Now," she said. "Why didn't you wake me up?"

"There wasn't time," Barbary said.

"Oh." Heather's scowl softened. "That's a good point."

Barbary squinted into starry space. "How do you know where to go?"

"It's not that hard. From where the station is now, and the direction and speed the ship's approaching, it has to be lined up with Betelgeuse, if Atlantis is directly behind us."

Barbary tried to imagine the geometry of the arrangement Heather described, with all the elements moving independently of one another, and came to the conclusion that it *was* hard, even if Heather was so used to it that she didn't know it.

She peered into the blackness, unable to make out anything but the bright multicolored points of stars.

Heather drew a piece of equipment from the control panel. It looked like a face mask attached to a corrugated rubber pipe. Heather fiddled with a control.

"Here," she said, and pushed the mask toward Barbary. "You can focus with this knob if you need to."

The image of the alien ship floated before her, a sharp, clear three-dimensional miniature, a jumble of spheres and cylinders, panels, struts, and irregularities, some with the hard-edged gleam of metal, some with the softer gloss of plastic, some with a rough and organic appearance, like tree bark. But for all Barbary knew, alien plastic looked like tree bark and their trees looked like steel. If they had trees, or plastic, or steel.

"Can you make it show Mick's raft?"

"That's harder," Heather said, "since I don't know what course Thea used. But I'll try." She bent over the mask, fiddling. "Hey, Barbary," she said.

"Yeah?"

"Were you really going to come out here all by yourself?"

"I guess so. I couldn't think of anything else to do."

"That was brave."

"Dumb, though," Barbary said. She never would have remembered the right controls, and she would have headed off in the wrong direction. "I guess you would have had to come out and get me and Mick both."

"Still, it was brave."

"Did you find Mick yet?" Barbary asked, embarrassed.

"Unh-uh, not yet."

"Can we use his transmitter?"

Heather glanced up, frowning.

"We could," she said, "but we can't, if you see what I mean. We'd have to use the computer, and if we turn it on it would probably lock our controls and take us home. But we'll find him, don't worry."

"Okay," Barbary said. "How long before we catch up to him, do you think?"

"It sort of depends on how fast the raft went out and how rapidly it was accelerating. Which I don't know. But it couldn't have been too fast, or it would use up all its fuel before it got to the ship. Then it wouldn't be able to maneuver, so it would just fly by very fast. Without much time to take pictures. So it has to be going slowly, instead. Anyway, we ought to catch up within a couple of hours. I don't want *us* to run out of fuel—and I don't want to get going so fast that we go right past without seeing Mick."

The raft hummed through silent space. Barbary kept expecting the stars to change, to appear to grow closer as the raft traveled toward them. But the stars were so distant that she would have to travel for years and years before even a few of them looked any closer or appeared to move, and even then they would still be an enormous distance away.

"Heather . . . "

"Yeah?"

"Thanks for coming with me," she said.

"Hey," Heather said, her cheerfulness touched with bravado. "What are sisters for?"

A red light on the control panel blinked on.

"Uh-oh," Heather said.

"What is it?"

"Radio transmission. Somebody from the station calling us. With orders to come back, probably."

They stared at the light. Heather reached for the radio headset.

Barbary grabbed Heather's hand. "If you answer them, they'll just try to persuade us to turn around."

"But we ought to at least tell them that it's us out here," Heather said.

"They probably already know. If they don't, maybe we ought to wait until they figure it out."

"Yoshi will be worried," Heather said sadly, "when he comes home, and he can't find us."

"We're going to have to transmit a message to the aliens anyway," Barbary said. "To tell them we don't mean to bother them, but Mick is in the first raft and we're coming out to rescue him. When we do that, they'll hear us back in Atlantis."

"Uh-huh." Heather gazed into the scanner. "I wonder why they don't want us to come near them? I wonder what they do when somebody does?"

"I guess they could blow us up with death-rays," Barbary said. "But that doesn't seem too civilized."

"And how are we going to explain cats to them? I wonder if they have pets? I wonder what they look like?"

"Maybe they're big cats themselves, like the aliens in *Jenny and the Spaceship*," Barbary said. "Did you read that?"

"Big *cats?*" Heather said. "That's silly, Barbary. The aliens come from some other star system. They evolved on a whole different planet. They probably don't even have the same chemistry we do. They might breathe cyanide or methane or something. Big *cats?*"

"Okay, okay, forget it," Barbary said. "It was just a book."

The radio light continued to glow. To Barbary, it seemed to be getting brighter and brighter, more and more insistent.

Heather finally put on the headset. When she turned on the radio, she spoke before a transmission from Atlantis could come through.

"Raft to alien ship, raft to alien ship. Um . . . hi. My sister Barbary and I—I'm Heather—are trying to rescue a . . . a sort of friend of ours who got stuck in the first raft by mistake. Now we can't make the raft turn around, so we have to catch up to it to get him." She hesitated. "Please don't be mad or anything. Over and out."

In the instant between the time Heather stopped transmitting and turned off the radio, the receiver burst into noise.

"—do you hear me? You girls get back here right now, or—"

Barbary recognized the voice of the vice president.

Heather clicked off the radio.

"He sounded pretty mad," she said. "I guess now they'll tell Yoshi where we are."

"Heather, what if the aliens try to call us? We won't be able to hear them, if we don't leave the radio turned on."

Heather raised one eyebrow and flicked the switch again.

"—return immediately, and you won't be punished. But if—"

She turned it off.

She shrugged cheerfully. "We wouldn't be able to hear the aliens anyway, with Atlantis broadcasting nonstop at us, unless the aliens just blasted through their signal. I'll try later—maybe the vice president will get tired of yelling at us."

"What do we do now?"

"We just wait," Heather said. "I'll keep looking for Mickey's raft. When we find it we'll know better what we need to do and how long it'll take."

"Let me help look," Barbary said.

"Okay."

Heather showed her how to search the star-field for anomalies. At first glance, they looked like stars. But if one looked at an anomaly at two different times, the bright speck would have moved in relation to the real stars. The scanner could save an image and display it alternately with a later view of the same area. An anomaly would blink from one place on the image to another, and the human eye could see the difference. A computer could, too, but it took processing time or a lot of memory, or both, to do what a person could do in an instant.

"Astronomers used to discover new planets and comets and things this way," Heather said. "You can also search by turning up the magnification, but that means you can only see a little bit of space at once. So unless you got really lucky, you'd spend days and days trying to find what you were looking for."

Barbary scanned for the alien ship. When she finally found it she felt pleased with herself, until she remembered how easily Heather had done the same thing.

"Shouldn't Mick's raft be right in between us and the alien ship?" Barbary asked.

"It could be," Heather said. "But it isn't. Nothing moves in straight lines in space, not when there are gravity fields to affect your course. Besides, I'm sure Thea didn't send her camera on a direct line to where the ship is now. She probably planned to arc around it. I mean, she wouldn't want to run into it. There's no way to tell exactly what course she chose. We could call and ask her—"

"As if she'd tell us—"

"She would. But I don't think the VIPs would let her."

"So we just keep looking?"

"Yeah."

Barbary let Heather have the scanner. She knew Heather could find Mick about a hundred times faster than she could.

"What's it like back on earth?" Heather said abruptly, without looking up. "What's it like to visit a farm, or camp out in the wilderness?" She waited quite a while, as Barbary tried to figure out how to answer her. Finally Heather said in a small voice, "Never mind. I didn't mean to pry."

"It's okay," Barbary said. "It isn't that. It's just a hard question to answer. There are so many different places and different things to see—only I haven't seen most of them. It's hard to get a permit to go out in the wilderness, and you need a lot of equipment, and that costs money. Nobody I knew ever did it."

"What about farms? Did you see cows and horses and stuff?"

"I've never been on a farm, either. There weren't any near where I lived, and they aren't like in movies. They're all automated. Big machines run them. Some of them are covered with plastic to keep the water and the heat in. A couple years ago I snuck off to a zoo. I saw a cow then. It looked kind of bored and dumb. Horses are prettier, but hardly anybody on farms has them anymore. Mostly, rich people keep them to ride."

"How about an ocean?"

"I never saw that, either."

"Oh."

"I wish I could tell you . . ."

"That's all right. I've talked to other people about it, and I've seen pictures and tapes. But I can't figure out what it would be like to see it myself."

"You know, Heather," Barbary said, "an awful lot of people talk about going to the mountains, or going to the ocean, but hardly anybody ever did it. Not anybody I knew, anyway."

"But they could have gone if they wanted."

"Yeah. They could have."

"I usually don't care. But sometimes I wish I could go see the mountains or the ocean, or blue sky."

"Your sky is prettier."

"I bet a blue one would be easier to find a raft in." Heather raised her head from the scanner. She looked exhausted. She had dark circles under her eyes. Barbary felt afraid for her.

"Want me to look?" Barbary asked.

"I'll do it a while longer, then it'll be your turn," Heather said. She stretched, and hunched and relaxed her shoulders a couple of times. "I don't suppose you brought along any sandwiches or anything, did you?"

"No," Barbary said. "I didn't even think of it."

"Oh, well. There are some rations in the survival ball. But they're pretty boring. Probably we should wait till we're really hungry before we use them."

Barbary thought she would get sick if she tried to eat. She felt empty and scared.

Heather bent over the scanner once more. "Hey! Look at this!"

Barbary peered into the scanner.

"I just see stars."

"Keep looking." Heather touched the blink control.

In the center of the picture, one of the bright points jumped. "Is that Mick?"

"Has to be," Heather said.

Barbary flashed the control again; again the image jumped. "Now zoom in."

Barbary did so. The raft appeared. The airless distance of space transmitted details sharp and clear, but all she could find was the silver and plastic shape of the raft, and the shadows of Thea's contraption inside. Nothing moved.

"There it is!" she said. She magnified it even more. "I don't see Mick though."

"Let me look."

Heather teased the scanner controls.

"Can you see him?"

"Umm . . . no," Heather said. "I can't. But there's a lot of stuff in there. He'd practically have to sit on top of it for me to find him."

"He's probably sitting under it," Barbary said. "Yowling. Or growling like a wildcat."

Heather laughed. "I bet you're right."

Barbary felt both overjoyed and terrified. Heather had found Mick—but Barbary would not be able to stop worrying till she saw for herself that he was all right.

"Where is he?" she asked. "Right in front of us?"

"No, he's kind of over to the side." Heather pointed. "Thea must have planned to circle all the way around the alien ship, then follow it as far as she could. I'm going to have to turn us pretty hard. Are you strapped in?"

"Uh-huh. How long will it take to get there?"

"A couple of hours, maybe. I'm just guessing, though."

"How do we get him when we get there?"

"We can't. There's no safe way to open a raft in space unless everybody inside is in a space suit or a survival ball, and Mick couldn't get in one by himself. So we'll stick out our claws and grab his raft and turn us both around, and go back."

"Oh," Barbary said. She had been hoping there was some way of getting from one raft to another. But at least she would be able to look inside and see Mick.

"Hang on."

The raft plunged into free fall as Heather cut the acceleration. Barbary flung her hands out before her, for it really did feel as if she were falling. The steering rocket flared on, the stars swung, and the rocket on the other side counteracted their spin. Now, Barbary knew, they were traveling in the same direction as before, but Heather had turned the raft a few degrees to the left.

Heather applied some thrust to the raft. The new acceleration would add to their previous velocity, changing their direction and speed so they would be heading more nearly toward Mickey.

Getting to the right spot in space took a lot of care and calculation. It would have been much easier if they could have flown the raft like an airplane, or like a spaceship in a movie, banking into turns and *swooshing* from place to place. But in a vacuum, without any air, ships could not bank into turns or *swoosh*.

"I don't want to kill any more velocity than I have to," Heather said. "It takes too much fuel. So I'll probably have to correct our course a bunch of times. But for now we're sort of heading for where Mick ought to be when we get there."

Barbary tried to figure out how that worked. It sounded suspiciously like a math word problem, which she had never been very good at. She had never seen the point of figuring out when two trains would pass each other when the only trains left were tourist attractions that she had never ridden anyway. But being able to figure out in her head how to meet another raft in space would be useful. She wished she had paid more attention to word problems in school, and she wondered if it was too late for her to learn how to do what Heather could do.

"Hey, Heather—Heather!"

Heather jerked up from the scanner, blinking and confused.

"Huh? What? I'm awake!" She stopped, abashed.

"No, you're not," Barbary said. "You fell asleep sitting up! Heather . . . look . . . maybe . . ." With a shock, she realized how much danger she and Mick had put Heather in.

"Oh, no!" Heather said. "Don't even say it! We're not turning around and going back like we just came out here to make trouble and then lost our nerve!"

Barbary hunched in her seat. She felt miserable.

"I'm afraid you're going to get sick," she said.

"I'm okay! I'm just a little tired!" Heather snapped. Her expression softened. "Look," she said. "I don't have to do anything for a while. I could take a nap, and you could keep an eye on the scanner. I'll set it so the image of Mick's raft will get closer and closer to the center till we intercept it. If it goes past the center of the focus, wake me up to correct the course." She showed Barbary the faint band of color outlining a square in the center of the scanner. The other raft lay at the left edge of the screen; it moved, almost imperceptibly, centerward.

"That sounds easy enough," Barbary said.

Heather grinned. "It's a lot easier than trying to sleep in a raft, that's for sure." She squirmed around, trying to get comfortable.

"Lie down crosswise and put your head in my lap," Barbary said. "I'll try not to bonk you with the scanner."

"Okay."

Barbary took off her jacket and tucked it around Heather's shoulders. Heather curled up under it, hiding her eyes from the light of the control panel. Her position still did not look very comfortable, but within a few minutes she was fast asleep.

Barbary looked around. Far behind her, spinning, lit from behind, the station grew smaller. The earth and the moon each showed only a slender crescent of light, for Barbary was on their night sides. The raft's automatic shield hid the sun and prevented it from blinding her.

Even in the observation bubble of the transport ship, she had never felt so alone and so remote. Beauty surrounded her, a beauty too distant and too enormous for her ever to reach or comprehend. She gazed out at the stars for a very long time, till she realized how long she had been staring. She quickly grabbed the scanner. To her relief, the other raft still lay within the field, halfway to the center of the focus.

Barbary increased the magnification, but that sent the raft all the way off the screen. If she moved the focus, she might not get it back to the place where Heather had aimed it. That also meant she could not use the scanner to find the alien ship, to see if it was doing anything threatening or even simply different.

Heather slept on. The radio receiver's light never flickered from its brilliant red. Trying to keep her attention on the scanner, Barbary forced herself to remain calm. But worry raced through her mind. She began to wonder if perhaps the aliens, and not the space station, might be trying to call the raft: to tell her they understood, everything was all right; to tell her they did not understand, please try to explain more clearly; or to tell her they understood, but they did not believe her and did not trust her and did not care anyway, and were going to shoot both rafts with death-rays.

She put on the headset and turned on the radio and the transmitter.

"This is the second raft calling, in case you didn't hear us before." She whispered, trying not to wake Heather. "We're coming out to rescue the first raft so it won't bother you. It's a mistake that it's out here, and we're really sorry. We're trying to fix things."

She turned off the transmitter, leaving the channel open for just a moment.

"Barbary!" Yoshi said. "Is Heather all right?"

"You two turn around and—"

The vice president's voice faded as Barbary cut the power to the radio without replying. She would have liked to reassure Yoshi, but she was afraid to get into a fight with any of the adults, especially Yoshi. Yoshi could say things that would make her want to turn around and go back, so he would not be so disappointed with her.

She glanced behind the raft. The science station was a bright turning toy, part lit, part shadowed, spinning between the more distant crescents of the earth and the moon.

Before her, space lay beautiful but still. Somehow the stars reminded her of snow early in the morning, before dawn, in a quiet, windless winter. She peered into the scanner to reassure herself that the other raft was still there. She squinted, searching for any sign of Mick. But his raft drifted onward, showing no signs of life.

She yawned, then shook her head to wake herself up. She could not go to sleep, though Heather's steady breathing in the silence of the little ship had a hypnotic effect. She yawned again. She pinched herself, hard.

A glimmer of light on metal caught her gaze.

Off to the left, far away but as clear as a close-up model, Mick's raft crept along. Now that she had found it, Barbary did not understand how she could have failed to see it for so long. She could tell it was in motion; she could tell her own raft was approaching it, slowly and at a tangent. In the scanner, the image had touched the outer edge of the focus square.

She started to touch Heather's shoulder, but decided against waking her yet. They still had quite a way to go before their raft intercepted Mick's, and Heather needed the rest.

Still careful not to change the direction of the scanner, Barbary increased the magnification. Now she could see part of the raft in the center of the frame. But the transparent roof had not yet come into view. Barbary stared at the image, willing it to move faster so she could look inside. It crept onto the screen, appearing to move sideways because of its orientation and because she was approaching it from behind and to one side. She wished she could see its front. Often, when Mick had ridden in a car, he crouched up front looking through the windshield. But she supposed he would have trouble crouching on the dashboard of a raft, without any gravity.

Something glided through the picture.

Her heart pounding with excitement, Barbary bent closer over the scanner.

"Mick," she whispered, "hey, come past again, okay?" The portion of the image taken up by transparent raft roof increased. She held her breath.

As if he knew she was coming after him, Mick brought himself up short against the plastic and peered directly at her. He opened his mouth wide. If they had not been separated by the vacuum of space, she would have heard his plaintive yowl.

"Okay," she said, laughing with relief. "I'm coming to get you, you dumb cat."

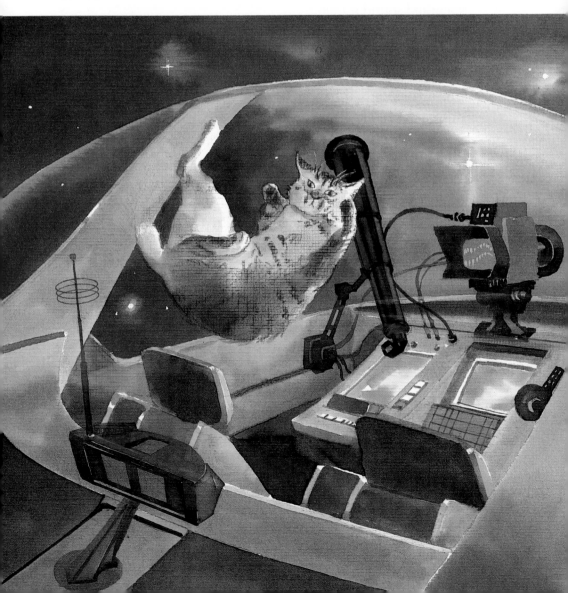

The scanner grew foggy. She had come so close to crying that she had misted up the mask. She sat up and reached into it to rub away the condensation with her sleeve. She glanced outside to check the position of Mick's raft.

To her shock, it—and Mick, looking at her—lay no more than twenty meters away. She was gaining on it.

"Heather!" she cried.

She pushed the scanner out of the way and pulled her jacket off Heather's shoulders. She shook her, but Heather remained sound asleep.

"Heather, come on!"

Barbary did not intend to come this far and lose Mick. She did not know if they could turn around and come back for him if they passed his raft. She jammed her hands into the grasps of the claw controls. She reached out; the grapples extended from beneath the raft. She opened her fingers and closed them; the claws followed her motion.

The distance between the rafts diminished to ten meters, then to five.

Barbary reminded herself again and again that the key to doing anything in space was to do it calmly and smoothly. She did not feel calm. She felt terrified and ignorant. Sweat rolled into her eyes. She could not take her hands from the grasps, and she was afraid to take her gaze off the other raft long enough to lean down and rub her forehead on her sleeve.

"Heather—!"

Even if Heather woke now, there was no time for her to take over the controls. As her raft approached Mick's, so much faster than it had seemed to be moving when they were far away, Barbary grabbed for it.

As she clenched her fingers in the grappler controls, the two rafts came together with a tremendous, wrenching *clang*. Barbary gasped, fearing she had rammed hard enough to breach the hull of Mick's raft or her own. The ships began a slow tumble. Around them, the stars spun. Barbary squeezed her eyes tight shut. That was even worse. She opened her eyes again. The claws kept the two vehicles clamped tight together. She could no longer see Mick, for he was underneath her. But as the reverberations of the crash faded, she heard, transmitted through the hulls, Mick's angry, objecting howl.

She laughed with relief. The motion of the rafts was beginning to make her dizzy, though, and the rafts would continue to tumble till someone used the steering rockets to counteract the spiraling twist. Heather would know how to do it.

"Hey, Heather—"

Usually when Heather wanted to sleep some more, she muttered and pulled her blanket over her head. This time, she lay still.

"Heather?"

Heather's hands felt cold as ice and her skin was very pale. Frightened, Barbary leaned down and put her ear to her sister's chest. Her heartbeat sounded weak and irregular. Barbary wished she knew what it was supposed to sound like, or what it usually sounded like.

Afraid to try to wake her again, Barbary covered her with her jacket and pillowed Heather's head in her lap.

"It's okay," she said. "I got Mick, I can get us back." She studied the controls. She would have to figure out how to make the ship stop tumbling, then turn it around. She wished she did not feel so dizzy—

Then she thought, You dummy! If you turn on the radio and the computer, back at Atlantis they'll send out the signal to bring us back. It's what they've wanted all along!

She threw the two switches, and got ready to be bawled out. The radio remained silent.

As the raft rotated, an enormous shape slid past the roof.

The rotation of the raft slowed, though Barbary felt no vibration from the steering rockets.

The huge shape slid into view again, the rotation stopped, and Barbary found herself gazing through the roof at the looming alien ship.

Barbary put her arms across Heather as if she could protect her.

Slowly, the raft moved toward the irregular, multicolored hull.

The alien ship drew the raft closer, growing larger and larger till its expanse of incomprehensible shapes stretched as far as Barbary could see.

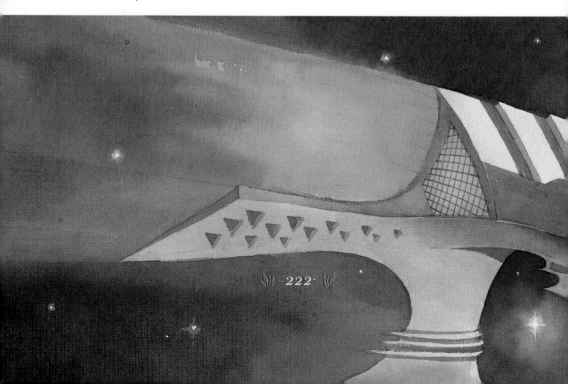

Trembling, she hugged Heather closer. She wrapped her jacket closer around her sister's shoulders, trying to keep her warm. The raft slid between two irregular projections from the alien ship's hull: a spire taller than any building on earth, covered with delicate strands and symbols, and a wavy, faceted shape resembling the crystals that form around a string suspended in a supersaturated solution of sugar and water.

Roof first, Barbary's raft floated toward a wide black slash in the ship's hull. If she did not keep telling herself she was going "up," she felt as if she were falling, upside down and in slow motion.

Intense darkness closed in around her.

The raft's control panel spread a ghostly light on Heather's pale face and Barbary's hands. She heard the echo of Mick's plaintive miaow, and the feathery whisper of Heather's breath.

A faint chime rang, growing louder and closer. Barbary blinked, trying to figure out if she only imagined light outside

the raft, or if she were seeing a glow as gentle as dawn. The ringing reached a pleasant level and remained there, while the light brightened till Barbary could see. She had weight as well, but she had not noticed when the gravity appeared. She felt as if she weighed as much as she did on earth, and this increased her concern for Heather.

Her raft hung in a round room whose surface glistened like mother-of-pearl. The columns supporting the ceiling looked like frozen waterfalls or translucent pillars of melted glass. She searched for the opening that had let her in, but it had closed or sealed itself up. From the wind-chime sound transmitted to her through the raft's body, she decided she must be surrounded by an atmosphere, but she did not know if it was oxygen or—as Heather had speculated—methane or cyanide. She had no way to tell whether it was safe to breathe, or poisonous.

Mick miaowed again, louder.

"It's okay, Mick," she said. She swallowed hard, trying to steady her voice. "It's going to be okay."

"Do you hear us?"

The radio spoke with the beautiful voice of the alien's first message to Atlantis.

"Yes," she whispered, her throat dry. "Can you hear me?"

"We sense you. Will you meet us?"

"I want to. I really do," Barbary said. "But I have to get Heather into zero gravity and back to the space

224

station. She's sick and I can't wake her up. The gravity's too strong for her here. Besides, all the important people are waiting to meet you, and they'll be really angry if I see you first."

"But," the voice said, "you have already seen us."

Barbary stared around the chamber, looking for creatures, great ugly things like the aliens in old movies, or small furry things like the aliens in books. They must be hiding behind the tall glass pillars.

The gravity faded till it was barely enough to give Barbary's surroundings a "down" and an "up."

"Is this gravity more comfortable for you?"

"Yes," Barbary said. "Thanks."

"We believed we calibrated your gravity correctly."

"You did," Barbary said. "At least it felt okay to me. But Heather . . . Heather has to live in lower gravity. Won't you let us go? She's sick! Anyway, I can't see you—" She stopped, amazed.

Though she had not seen them move, the crystal columns had come closer. They clustered around her. Their rigid forms remained upright, yet they gave the impression of bending down like a group of worried aunts or friendly trees. A long row of crystalline fibers grew along the side of each column. The fibers quivered rapidly, vibrating against and stroking the main body of each being, producing the wind-chime voices.

"Oh," she said. "Oh. I *do* see you. You're beautiful!"

"We will loose your craft if you wish," the voice on the radio said. "But our ship will reach your habitat before your vessel could fly to it, and here the gravity can be controlled."

"Can you hurry? I'm really worried about Heather."

"We will hurry."

Barbary listened to Heather's rapid, irregular heartbeat.

"Can't you help her?" she said to the aliens. She remembered all the movies she had seen where people got hurt and aliens healed them. "Can't you make her well? Aliens are supposed to be able to make people well!"

"But we have only just met you," one of the aliens said, perplexed and regretful. "We know little of your physiology. Perhaps in a few decades, if you wish us to study you . . ."

Barbary thought she should have learned by now not to expect anything to work the way it did in books or movies. She leaned over Heather again, willing her to awaken.

Heather's eyelids fluttered.

"Barbary . . . ?"

Heather opened her eyes. She sounded weak, confused, and tired.

"It's okay, Heather. Anyway, I think it is—what about you?"

"I feel kind of awful. What happened?"

"We're on the alien ship."

A spark of excitement brought some of the color back to her sister's cheeks. She struggled to a sitting position.

"Are there aliens?" Heather whispered. She was shivering. Barbary chafed her cold hands and helped her put on the jacket.

"There are other beings," the gentle voice said. "We hope not to be alien, one to the other, for very long. Will you meet us?"

"Can we breathe your air?" Heather hugged the jacket around her.

"It is not our air. We do not use air. It is your air. You should find it life-sustaining, uninfectious, and sufficiently warm to maintain you."

Barbary gingerly cracked the seal of the roof-hatch. Warm, fresh air filled the raft. Heather took a deep breath. Her shivering eased.

"If you join us," a voice said, no longer from the radio but from one of the crystalline beings, "then we may rotate your vehicles and release the small person in the lower craft. It does not respond to our communications in an intelligible fashion, and it appears to be quite perturbed."

Barbary could not help it: she laughed. Heather managed to smile. Barbary picked her up—her weight was insignificant in this gravity—and carried her from the raft. The aliens made a spot among them for her; they slid across the mother-of-pearl floor as if, like starfish, they had thousands of tiny sucker-feet at their bases. The floor gave off a comforting warmth. Barbary laid Heather on the yielding surface.

"I'm okay, I really am," Heather said. She tried to sit up, but she was still weak. Barbary helped her, letting Heather lean back against her. Heather gazed at the aliens. "Holy cow."

Mick's furry form hurtled across the space between the rafts and Barbary. He landed against her with all four feet extended and stopped himself by hooking his claws into her shirt. Somehow he managed to do it without touching her skin with his claws. He burrowed his head against her, and she wrapped her arms around him and laid her cheek against his soft fur.

"Boy, Mick," she whispered, "did you cause a lot of trouble."

STARS
Seymour Simon

Stars are huge balls of hot, glowing gases. Our sun is a star. It is just an ordinary star, not the biggest nor the brightest. But the sun is the star that is nearest to our planet Earth. Earth is part of the sun's family of planets, moons, and comets called the Solar System. All of the other stars that we see in the sky are much farther away from Earth. The stars are so far away from us that even through powerful telescopes they look like small points of light.

People long ago gave names to the brighter stars and learned where and when to look for them. They also gave names to the constellations, groups of stars that seem to form patterns in the sky. Usually these constellations were named after gods, heroes, or animals.

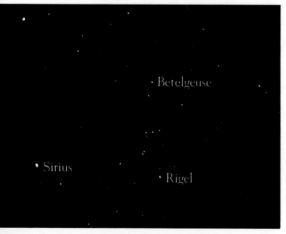

The photograph shows the constellation of Orion, the Hunter. Orion is visible during winter evenings. Look for the three bright stars in a row that form the belt of Orion. The bright red star in the upper left of Orion is named Betelgeuse (most people call it "beetle juice"). The brilliant

Kyle Cudworth, Yerkes Observatory

blue-white star in the lower right is named Rigel. The brightest star in the sky is Sirius, the Dog Star. It is just to the lower left of Orion in the constellation of Canis Major, the Big Dog.

Thousands of years ago Orion looked different than it does today. And thousands of years in the future it will look different than it does now. That's because stars move in space. They move very rapidly, ten or more miles per second. But the stars are so far away from us that we do not notice their motion in our lifetimes.

Imagine traveling in a spaceship going ten miles a second. Even at that speed, it would still take you about three and a half months to reach the sun. But it would take more than seventy thousand *years* to reach the next nearest star, Alpha Centauri.

Alpha Centauri is about twenty-five trillion miles away. There are other stars *millions* of trillions of miles away. These numbers are so big that they are hard to understand. Measuring the distance between the stars in miles is like measuring the distance around the world in inches.

Because of the great distances between stars, scientists measure with the light-year instead of the mile. Light travels at a speed of about 186,000 miles every second. A light-year is the distance that light travels in one year: a bit less than six trillion miles. Alpha Centauri is a little more than four light-years away. The stars shown in this giant cloud of gas in the constellation of Orion are fifteen hundred light-years away.

NOAO

How many stars do you think you can see on a clear, dark night? Can you see thousands, millions, countless numbers? You may be surprised that in most places only about two thousand stars are visible without a telescope.

When the great scientist Galileo looked through his low-power telescope in the year 1610, he saw thousands and thousands of stars that no one on earth had ever seen before. As more powerful telescopes were made, millions and millions of other stars were seen.

What looks like clouds in the photograph of the Milky Way galaxy below are really millions of stars too far away to be seen as separate points of light. With powerful telescopes we can see that the stars are as many as the grains of sand on an ocean beach.

Stars are born in giant clouds of gas and dust called nebulas. Most of the gas is hydrogen with a small amount of helium. Over millions of years, gravity pulls the gas and dust

NOAO

particles together and squeezes them so that they heat up. When the gas gets hot enough, it sets off a nuclear reaction like that of a super hydrogen bomb and a star is born. This computer-colored photograph shows a newborn star (*arrow*) in the cloud of gas and dust known as Barnard 5.

Stars change as they grow older. For example, young stars (10 to 200 million years old) are very hot—with surface temperatures of more than 12,000 degrees (F)—and are usually blue or blue-white in color. Middle-aged stars like our sun are yellow and not as hot—10,000 degrees (F).

After about ten billion years stars begin to run out of their hydrogen fuel. Most of these old stars collapse upon themselves and they get hotter and hotter. Then, like a piece of popcorn when it "pops," the stars balloon out and become hundreds of times larger. They become what are known as red giant stars.

A red giant star may be 40 or 50 million miles across. Some are even larger. Betelgeuse is a red supergiant star 250 million miles across. If Betelgeuse were put in place of our sun in the center of the Solar System, it would swallow up Mercury, Venus, Earth, and Mars.

Some older stars go through a stage where they keep growing and then shrinking. These stars are called variable stars because at times they appear bright and at other times they are dim.

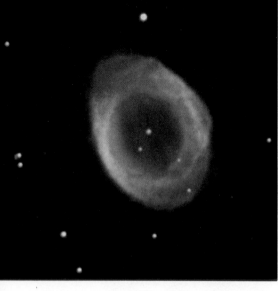

NASA

Other older stars shoot out a large cloud of gas into space. These stars are called planetary nebulas because through low-power telescopes they look like round planets. This photograph taken with a high-power telescope shows the real nature of a planetary nebula. This is the Ring Nebula in the constellation Lyra.

Finally, older stars cool and start collapsing. They shrink down to about the size of a small planet and are called white dwarf stars. As the white dwarfs slowly cool off they become black dwarf stars. And then the stars are dead.

Sometimes a star, usually a white dwarf, suddenly explodes and becomes much brighter. To people long ago it looked like a new bright star had appeared in the sky. They called the star a nova (*nova* means "new"). Even though most novas are too far away for us to see, scientists think that two or three dozen novas appear in the Milky Way every year.

Much rarer are the gigantic explosions known as supernovas. A supernova star flares up and becomes millions of times brighter than normal.

A supernova may appear only once every few hundred years. In the year 1054, Chinese astronomers saw a supernova in the constellation of Taurus. Today we can see the gaseous remains of that exploding star. We call it the Crab Nebula.

NASA

Some supernovas shatter completely, leaving behind only the wispy gases of a nebula. But a few supernovas leave a small, tightly packed ball of particles called a neutron star. A tiny drop of a neutron star would weigh a billion tons on earth.

The sudden collapse of a supernova causes a neutron star to spin very rapidly and give off a beam of X-ray radiation. Like the beam from a lighthouse, we can detect the X rays as a pulse. So a rotating neutron star is called a pulsar.

This X-ray photograph shows a pulsar in the middle of the Crab Nebula. The X rays from the pulsar in the Crab blink on and off thirty times every second. The star is visible when the X rays are "on" and invisible when the X rays are "off."

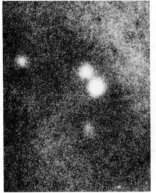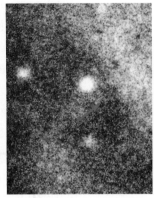

NOAO

Some stars are much larger than the average star. When such a massive star cools and collapses, it becomes something very special. The star is crushed together by the huge weight of the collapsing gases. Gravity keeps squeezing and squeezing until the star seems to disappear. The star has become a black hole.

Anything passing too close to a black hole will be pulled into it and never get out again. Even light is pulled in and cannot escape, so a black hole is invisible. Yet, scientists think they have located several black holes.

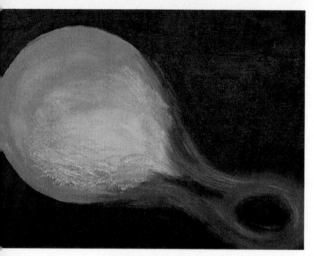

This drawing is of a double star called Cygnus X-1. Only one of the stars is visible: a hot, blue giant star. Near it is a black hole that pulls gases from its neighbor. As the gases are sucked in they become so hot that they give off huge amounts of X rays. Some scientists think that there are many such black holes scattered throughout space.

Our sun is an unusual star. It does not have any nearby stars circling it. Most stars have one or more companion stars and they revolve around each other. The star groups are so far from us that most look like single points of light to our eyes.

About half of all the stars we can see are double, or binary, stars. There are also many groups with three, four, a dozen, or even more stars in them. These groups of stars move through space together like flocks of birds in flight. Scientists think that the stars in such a group were all formed at the same time.

Very large groups of stars are called star clusters. This is a photograph of the Pleiades, an open cluster of stars. It contains several hundred stars that form a loose group with no special shape. These are young stars and they are surrounded by clouds of gas and dust.

NOAO

NASA

Here is a different kind of star cluster called a globular cluster. A globular cluster contains many thousands, or even millions, of stars very close together.

This is the great globular cluster known as M.13 in the constellation of Hercules. It is visible just as a dot of light to the naked eye. But through a telescope we can see that it has at least a million stars. Most of these stars are very old and they have stayed together throughout their lifetime.

The biggest star clusters of all are called galaxies. Galaxies are the largest kind of star systems. Our sun and its planets are a member of a galaxy called the Milky Way. There are more than one hundred billion stars in the Milky Way galaxy.

The sun is located almost out on the edges of the Milky Way. All the stars in the Milky Way whirl around the center of the galaxy, each at its own speed. The sun along with the Solar System moves at about 150 miles a second around the center of the galaxy. But the galaxy is so big that the sun takes about 225 million years to go around once.

Are there planets circling other stars in our galaxy? The answer is almost definitely yes. This picture shows a ring of material surrounding the star Beta Pictoris. This material is thought to be a young solar system in the making.

235

Jet Propulsion Laboratory

Planets form at the same time and from the same gases as do stars. So scientists think it is likely that some or even many stars have planets circling them. If even a tiny percentage of these planets are similar to Earth, then there may be millions of Earth-like planets in the galaxy.

Do any of these planets have life on them? No one knows. But scientists are using radio telescopes to listen for signals of intelligent life in outer space. They think the signals will come in the form of radio waves much like those of our own radios and televisions. So far scientists have not found anything, but they are not discouraged. Until they have examined every star that may have planets they won't know for sure.

The Milky Way is only one galaxy among millions of others in the universe. Galaxies — large and small, single or in

NOAO

groups and clusters, and in many different shapes — are found in every direction.

The Andromeda galaxy, shown here, is a spiral galaxy with almost twice as many stars as there are in the Milky Way. The Andromeda galaxy lies in far distant space, almost twelve quintillion miles away. That's 12,000,000,000,000,000,000! Light from this galaxy has been traveling for more than two million years by the time we see it in our telescopes.

How many galaxies are there in the universe? No one knows. But scientists think that there are about one hundred billion other galaxies. And each one of these galaxies contains hundreds of thousands of millions of stars.

Many mysteries confront us in the distant reaches of space. Beyond most of the galaxies that we can see with our largest telescopes are bright starlike objects called quasars. Each quasar gives off more than one hundred times the energy of all the stars in the Milky Way galaxy put together.

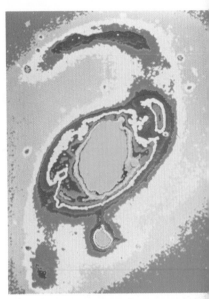

This is a computer-colored photo of a quasar-galaxy pair. Scientists think that quasars may be the centers of young galaxies that are just forming. Light from most quasars has been traveling for ten to fifteen billion years by the time it reaches Earth. That means that we are viewing quasars as they were ten to fifteen billion years ago, just after the universe began.

This photograph of Betelgeuse is the first ever to show the surface of a star other

NOAO

than the sun. Powerful telescopes orbiting above Earth's atmosphere may soon show us the very edges of the universe

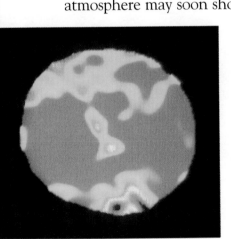

and the beginning of time itself. Will all our questions about stars then be answered? It's not likely. Each mystery that we solve about space seems to lead to many more unsolved questions about the nature of the universe.

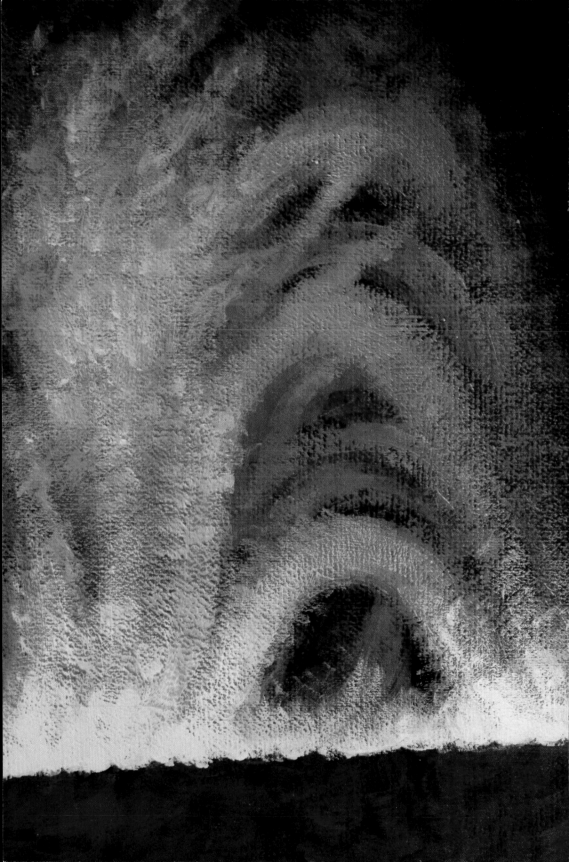

SUN

Myra Cohn Livingston
illustrated by
Leonard Everett Fisher

Space
is afire
with bursts of bubbling gas,

colliding atoms,
boiling wells
and solar flares

spewing

from a burning star, the sun.

Ninety-three million miles away

this mass,
quaking inferno,
pluming arcs and bridges

roars;

a giant bomb
exploding
hydrogen.

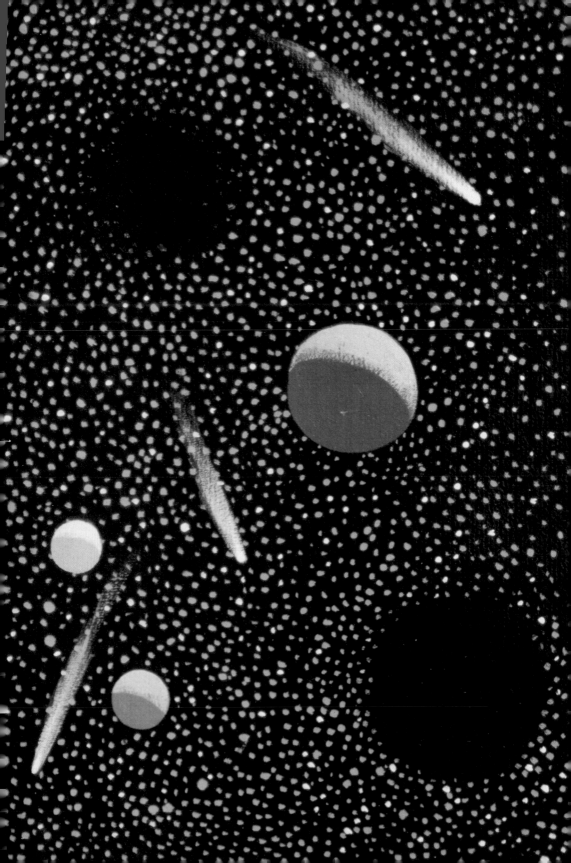

SECRETS

Myra Cohn Livingston
illustrated by Leonard Everett Fisher

Space keeps its secrets
hidden.
It does not tell.

Are black holes time machines?
Where do lost comets go?

Is Pluto moon or planet?

How many, how vast
unknown galaxies beyond us?

Do other creatures
dwell   on distant spheres?

Will we ever know?

Space is silent.
It seldom answers.

But we ask.

BIBLIOGRAPHY

Ancient Astronomy by Isaac Asimov. This book from the series Isaac Asimov's Library of the Universe briefly describes the history of astronomy from prehistoric times until the time of Galileo.

Anno's Medieval World by Mitsumasa Anno. How did the discoveries of Galileo and Columbus change ways of thinking about the world and the universe? Beautiful illustrations help to tell the story.

Astronomy for Every Kid: 101 Easy Experiments that Really Work by Janice VanCleave. Have fun while you learn the basic concepts of astronomy.

The First Travel Guide to the Moon: What to Pack, How to Go, and What to See When You Get There by Rhoda Blumberg. Take a trip to the moon with this imaginative guidebook.

The Nova Space Explorer's Guide: Where to Go and What to See by Richard Maurer. Explore the moon, the planets, and beyond with this book based on the popular television series.

Sky Above and Worlds Beyond by Judith Herbst. This introduction to studying the stars includes information about the astronomy of ancient Britons, Mayas, Egyptians, and Native Americans.

To Space & Back by Sally Ride with Susan Okie. An astronaut tells what it's like to live on a space shuttle.

A Wrinkle in Time by Madeleine L'Engle. In this popular book, L'Engle describes a trip through space and time.

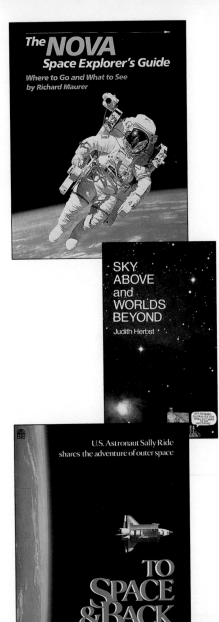

244

FAMILY
HERITAGE

245

Alice and Billy Rivers and their children.

IN TWO WORLDS:
A YUP'IK ESKIMO FAMILY
from the book by
Aylette Jenness and Alice Rivers
photographs by Aylette Jenness

Long Ago

Alice and Billy Rivers live with their children in the small town of Scammon Bay, Alaska, on the coast of the Bering Sea. They are Yup'ik Eskimos. Their story really begins long, long ago.

Alice and Billy's parents, grandparents, great-grandparents, great-great-grandparents—all their ancestors for several thousand years—have always lived here. They were part of a small group of Yup'ik Eskimos whose home was this vast area of tidal flats bordering the sea, with, inland, marshes, ponds, creeks, and rivers lacing the flat treeless tundra, broken only by occasional masses of low hills.

Each year, as the northern part of the earth tilted toward the sun, the long hours of sunlight here melted the snow, melted the sea ice, melted the rivers, melted, even, the frozen land down to the depth of a foot or so. Briefly, for a few months, birds came from the south to lay their eggs and raise

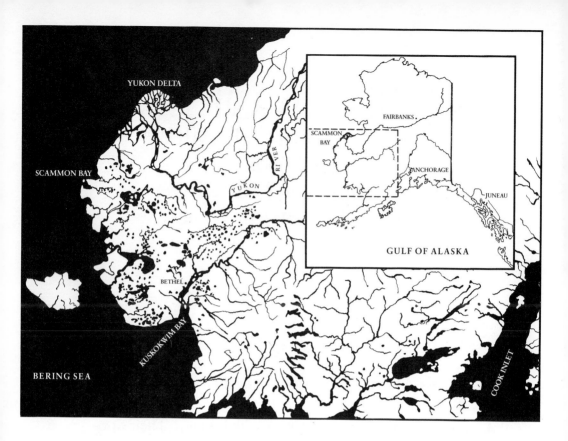

their young. The fish spawned, plants grew, berries ripened. And then the earth tilted away from the sun. Days grew shorter, the sun weaker, temperatures fell. The rain turned to snow, plants withered, birds flew south. Ponds, creeks, rivers, and finally even the Bering Sea froze, and layers of snow covered the whole landscape. Fish, sea mammals, and land animals all moved beneath thick blankets of ice and snow.

The small, scattered groups of Yup'ik Eskimos knew exactly how to survive here. Living as single families, or in small groups of relatives, they moved with the seasons to catch each kind of fish, bird, or mammal when and where each was most easily available. They harpooned the whales that migrated north along the coast in spring and south in the fall. They shot and snared birds nesting on the tundra, and they gathered the birds' eggs. They netted saltwater fish coming to lay their eggs in the rivers and creeks, and they caught freshwater fish moving beneath the ice of inland creeks. They trapped small mammals on the land for meat and for fur clothing. They knew where to find and how to catch dozens of different fish and animals for food, for clothing, even for light and heat for their small homes.

They had fire, but they didn't know how to use it to make metal. Everything they had they made themselves, with their hands, with stone, bone, or ivory tools—their many intricate snares and nets and traps, their boats and sleds, their homes and their clothing. Life was hard and precarious. Nothing was wasted.

Their mark on the land was light. Today their old sites are nearly part of the earth, not easy to see. These Yup'ik Eskimos didn't build monuments to gods or leaders. They believed that animals had spirits, and that the spirits survived the animals' death to inhabit other animals. After killing a seal, they put water in its mouth to show their caring and respect for it and to ensure that its spirit would return in the form of another seal another time. They made up stories and dances of awe, fear, and pleasure in the animals they knew so well.

They shared with each other, and no one was much better or worse off than anyone else. Families, or groups of families, had rights to certain places for hunting or fishing, but no one owned the land or its resources.

They knew no outsiders, no one different from themselves. During those hundreds and hundreds of years, their way of life changed very little. People followed in the footsteps of their ancestors, children learning from their parents the vast body of knowledge necessary for survival in this environment.

But during the last fifty years, their lives have changed enormously. And these changes are within the memory of the older people living here now.

Listen to Alice Rivers's mother, Mary Ann, describe her childhood. She speaks in Yup'ik, and one of her daughters, Leota, translates into English.

Mary Ann Remembers

"I was born, as I was told, in the late fall. My mother delivered me outside in the tundra, out in the open. My mother told me that after I was born I clutched some tundra moss and grass in my hand. I do not know why I was born outside, but it must have been because my mother was out in the tundra.

"When I was first aware of my surroundings, we lived on the other side of the mountains of Scammon Bay. The name of the place where I was born is called Ingeluk, and I think it's called this name because we are surrounded by small hills. We were the only people living in that area. We were secluded away from other people. There was my father, my mother, my two older sisters, and one older brother, and I am the youngest in the family.

"We lived in a sod house. The insides of our house had braided grass hanging on the walls as paneling. We had only one window, which was made out of dried seal guts, and it made a lot of noise when it was windy. Our floor was plain, hard, dried mud. Our beds were dried grass, piled high to keep us warm. We had no blankets. We mostly did with what we had at hand, and we used our parkas to keep us warm. I remember we had one kettle, a small half kerosene tank for our cooking pot, and the plates we had were carved from wood by my father.

"For light, we used seal oil when we had the oil, and it smoked a lot. Other times we had no light because we had no oil. I remember my mother cooked whitefish, and she carefully skimmed off the oil from the pot we had, and what she took out of the cooking pot we used in our oil lamp. The oil from the fish made pretty good light; it never smoked like the seal oil did. There were lots of stories being told, that's what we did during the evenings.

"Our main diet was fish, caught in my father's traps. There were times that we were really hungry. We were very poor. Sometimes when we woke up in the morning, we had nothing at all to eat.

"We didn't have any kind of bread. We did not know what coffee and tea were.

"I saw my first white man when we were traveling by our skin boat. I did not know who he was, but later on I was told that the white man was trading goods for fur or skins. Maybe I was fifteen years old when I saw an airplane.

"I liked the life we used to live a long time ago, but we were always in need of something. I would say we live in comfort now. I don't go in hunger now. I say both lives I led were good, and I like both."

Mary Ann grew up and married a man who lived nearby, Teddy Sundown. They began to raise their family in Keggatmiut, as Scammon Bay is known in Yup'ik. It was a good site, and a number of families settled there. They built their small log houses on the lower slope of a range of hills that rose out of the flat tundra. A clear stream, racing down the hillside, flowed into the river that wound along the base of the hills, and finally emptied into a wide, shallow bay of the Bering Sea. Mary Ann and Teddy still moved to seasonal camps to fish, trap, and hunt, but as the village grew, they began to spend more and more of the year there.

The United States government set up a school in Scammon Bay and hired a Yup'ik teacher. All of the children were expected to attend school.

Missionaries had come to convert the people from their traditional religion, and the village was divided between Catholics and Protestants. Two churches were built.

Alice was the fourth child born to Mary Ann and Teddy. She is shown at the age of ten, standing on the far right of her family. She speaks of growing up in Scammon Bay.

Gonzaga Collection, Yugtarvik Museum, Bethel, Alaska

Alice Remembers

"Our home was a one-room building. Our beds were together—Mom and Dad's bed and our bed. All of us kids slept together in one bed. No table—the tables came later on. We used to eat sitting on the floor, Eskimo way. Mom used to cook bread on top of the stove, 'cause there was no oven. To me it used to be the best bread I've eaten. Then as I grew older, we got a stove and oven, and she started baking bread.

"We ate bread, birds, dried herrings, clams, mussels, fish—boiled and frozen—seals, mink, muskrats. There were two stores. We bought shortening, flour, tea, coffee—just what we needed.

Jonathan Jenness

"We were always together. We'd go to church every morning. Mom would wake us up early, we'd go to mass. We never used to be lazy, we used to just go, get up and go, get up to a real cold morning, and by the time we were home, the house would be nice and warm.

"Right after church we used to go straight to school, all of us. I remember that learning to write my name was the hardest thing. I was maybe about six. We had Eskimo teachers. It was one room, and everything was there.

"After school, we'd have lots of things to do—bringing some wood in, dishes to wash, house to clean, babies to watch, water to pack. We had aluminum pails with handles. We used to run over to the stream and pack water until we had what we needed. In the winter we had to keep one hole in the ice open the whole winter. This was one of the things I used to do with my sisters, not only me.

"Planes came in maybe once a week with mail. We didn't know about telephones. We had a radio, just for listening. I think we listened to one station all the time. No TV.

"The teachers had a short-wave radio. If someone got sick, they would report us to the hospital. They would give us medication or send us to the hospital in Bethel."

Alice Grown Up

By the time Alice was an adult, Scammon Bay was a village of a hundred and fifty people, with twenty-five log and frame homes. For transportation, each family had a dog sled and team, and a boat for use in summer.

The government began to take a larger role in the Yup'ik villages. A new school was built, with living quarters for non-Eskimo teachers from outside of Alaska. Children were taught a standard public elementary school curriculum, which had little reference either to their own lives or to what they knew and didn't know about life outside Scammon Bay. They were forbidden to speak Yup'ik in school, in the belief that this would help them to learn English, and that learning English was very important.

A postmaster was hired from among the village men, and a custodian for the school. A health aide

Jonathan Jenness

◎ *255* ◎

was trained, and a small clinic built and stocked. More planes came to Scammon Bay, and it became easier to fly someone needing hospital care out—as long as the weather was good.

Government money became available for low-income families and for the elderly and disabled. There were few opportunities to earn cash, but almost all of the men in Scammon Bay were able to earn some money by hunting or trapping seals, mink, muskrats, and beaver and selling the skins to be made into luxury fur coats outside of Alaska. In summer they netted salmon in the river mouths north of Scammon Bay and sold this valuable fish to processors, who marketed it throughout the United States as smoked fish, or lox.

Each summer a freighter came up the coast from Seattle, Washington, with supplies for the villages. Everyone began to buy more factory-made goods. Some families bought stoves that burned fuel oil instead of relying on brush wood they cut nearby. Some bought windmills, which produced enough electricity for one or two light bulbs in their homes. Some bought snowmobiles, which enabled them to travel farther than they could by dog team to hunt and trap, but which, unlike dogs, required money for fuel and new parts.

And for the first time in the long history of the Yup'ik Eskimos, some people began to travel away from their homeland. Some teenagers went to boarding school in the state of Washington. Some men went to National Guard training, and some families moved away permanently, settling in Alaskan towns and cities, or even as far away as Oregon and California.

But most remained in Scammon Bay, and some new Yup'ik people came to live there from other towns.

NOW

Alice's life today is both very similar to that of her mother at the same age—and very different. Scammon Bay has grown and changed in many ways.

There are three hundred and fifty people in Scammon Bay now, living in fifty-six houses. Most of the old log homes are now used for storage, and many people, like the Riverses, have new houses provided by the government at low cost. A dish antenna relays television to all the homes. Satellite transmission enables families to make telephone calls anywhere in the world. Huge storage tanks hold fuel to run an electric generator that provides enough power for each home to have all the lights that people want. A water and sewage disposal system required building a water treatment plant and a lagoon on the tundra for waste water. The dump, full of cans, plastic, fuel drums, and broken machinery, is a reminder of the difficulty of disposing of modern trash.

For some years the state government made a great deal of money from taxes on oil found in Alaska, and this money paid for many of the modern conveniences in Scammon Bay and other rural towns. An airstrip was built so that planes could land more easily at all times of the year; it is regularly plowed in winter. Three small planes a day fly into Scammon Bay, bringing everything from cases of soft drinks to boxes of disposable diapers and, of course, the mail. A huge new gym has been built, and a new clinic, a preschool center, town offices, and a post office. The school is now run by the state, not the federal government, and goes all the way through the twelfth grade.

In spite of the changes, the traditional pattern of living from the land is still powerful. This can be seen most clearly as people move to seasonal camps during the summer months.

Fish Camp

On rocky Bering Sea beaches south of the village, herring come in immense schools to lay their eggs, and many families move there to fish for several weeks. Alice and Billy leave Scammon Bay with the children as soon as school is out for the summer.

Alice says, "Billy goes first and sets up our camp—tent, blankets, bed, clothes, pots and pans for cooking, and our grub. Then we go, maybe the third week in May. We pick spring greens, go hunting, take walks. We eat fish and fresh geese. It never gets dark when we're out camping, and it's fun."

Billy and other fishermen catch the herring in gill nets, both for their own use and to sell. Here the old ways and the new meet; Yup'ik Eskimos have been catching herring and drying them for winter food for hundreds of years, but it is only recently that they have been able to sell them for cash.

Billy sells his catch—as much as twenty thousand pounds of herring in a good year—to huge Japanese fish processing boats that wait out to sea. Prevented by law from fishing close to the coast of the United States, the Japanese buy the catch of Americans. The herring eggs are a great delicacy for the Japanese, who will pay very high prices for this special-occasion food. Most of the rest of the fish is ground up to make fertilizer.

Scammon Bay people still dry large numbers of herring for the winter, just as they have for hundreds of years. Split open, cleaned, and hung up to dry, the fish become a good-tasting, chewy, oily, protein-rich food that can last all winter. The fish that aren't caught in the nets lay their eggs on seaweed along the shores. The seaweed, dried, is also a traditional favorite food of Scammon Bay people. Soaked in water during the winter, it tastes fresh at a time when no fresh vegetables are available.

Jonathan Jenness

When the herring run is finished, people get ready to go north up the coast to the mouths of the rivers where salmon enter to lay their eggs. This is another chance to earn money. And Alice will dry a lot of salmon for the family's own use.

On the Weekends

During the school year, traditional ways of life are practiced mostly on the weekends. The end of each school week marks the beginning of two days of hunting and fishing for the whole Rivers family.

Alice says, "On the weekends, we get to go traveling with Billy. Usually we decide what we're going to do ahead of time, what's going to happen. Like if we want to go fishing, we go fishing, or hunting ptarmigans. We're out most of the day Saturday doing this and that."

This is where Billy becomes the teacher, training the kids in both the oldest methods of hunting and fishing, and the newest. Since the children spend so much time in school, this is an important time for them to learn how to survive as Eskimos.

"I teach my boys the way I've been taught, the way my dad taught me. What I think that's wrong, I try to do it better than my dad. And when I make a mistake, I try to correct it to my boys, so they'll do it better than I did.

"I start taking them out as soon as they're old enough—like in the boat, when they're old enough to sit down and take care of themselves. I tell them little things like taking the anchor out, putting the anchor back up. As soon as they understand our words, we teach them from there. If they show you something that they know, you'll know they learned it—and then they can start doing it by themselves.

"Each one of them that goes with me, I talk to them, I tell them about little things—what's dangerous, what's not dangerous. I tell them about melting ice—even though it looks good on the surface, some places you can't see when it's covered with snow, it's thin. That's where they fall through. I teach them what thin ice looks like, and how it looks when it's safe.

"Oscar's been going with me first, 'cause he's the oldest one, then Jacob. One of them will know more, the one that pays attention more, just like in school. The one that doesn't listen, or doesn't pay attention, he'll make more mistakes or get more scolding.

"Oscar was about seven or eight when I first let him shoot a gun. He got his first seal when he was maybe eight or nine. In the boat I did the driving, and I had him do the shooting. He got a young mukluk that was a baby in springtime. He shot it, and after he shot it, he looked at me, looked back, and he smiled. 'I catch it.' "

Oscar remembers this very clearly. He says, "My grandpa divided the seal up in circles and gave it to the old people." This is the traditional Yup'ik way of sharing a boy's first catch with the elders, still carried on, though motorboats have replaced kayaks, and rifles are used in place of thrown harpoons.

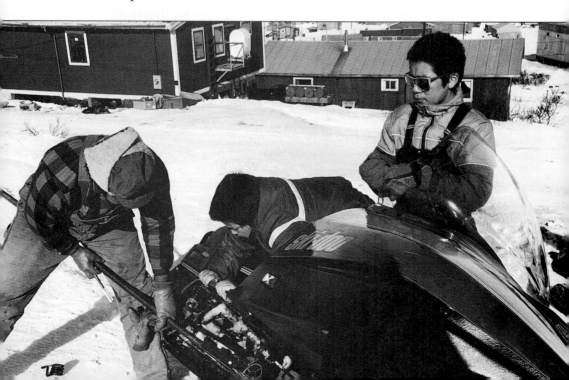

THE FUTURE

Alice and Billy know very well that life is changing fast here in Scammon Bay, and they want their children to be prepared for this.

Alice says, "When I was a kid, I used to do things with my mom. I used to watch her sew. Now I try to have Mattie knit, crochet, make things, but she thinks it's too boring. She knows how to do it, but she can't sit and look at one thing for a long time. I can't even teach her how to sew a skin. She doesn't have any patience.

"Now there's so many other things going on. In our time there was no basketball, no Igloo [community center], hardly any dances."

Billy says, "When I was Billy Junior's age, I used to run maybe twenty or thirty times around a pond with my little wooden boat. Just run around, play with it, put mud inside of it, and run around. I'd never think of TV, it wasn't in my mind.

"Everything is not the same here in Alaska, not like before. Things are changing. Things are getting more expensive. Most of the people are depending on more jobs. I mean working, you have to have a job.

"I talk to the kids, I just say what we'd like them to do. I tell them, 'If you go to school, and be smart over there, and try to learn what you're taught, you guys will have good jobs, and good-paying jobs. I want you to have good-paying jobs, so we'll have the things that we need, anything we need'; like this I talk to them.

"I'd be happy to have them travel to see other countries, to have them learning something that's Outside—*if* they have a job. 'Cause Outside there's many people without jobs, no home. Here it's okay, as we help each other here in the villages.

"We get after the kids for not doing their homework. We want them to be more educated, more than us. I mean, learn more. I only went up to the fifth grade."

Alice agrees. She adds "I want them to learn other ways—Outside ways. And I want them to learn our ways, too—hunting for our kind of foods. We can't have store-bought food all the time. I want them to learn both ways."

Looking down on Scammon Bay from the hill, it seems like a very small settlement, nearly lost in the huge expanse of tundra around it. From this distance it doesn't look so different from the Scammon Bay of Alice's childhood. Yet it is invisibly connected to the whole world now. And so is the Rivers family.

MEET AYLETTE JENNESS AND
ALICE RIVERS, AUTHORS
*Photographer and writer Aylette
Jenness met Alice Rivers when Jenness lived in
Scammon Bay, Alaska, during the 1960s.
Jenness first came to Alaska to work on her
books* Gussuk Boy *and* Dwellers of the
Tundra, *both of which were about the people of
Scammon Bay. When Jenness returned to
Alaska for a visit more than twenty years later,
the two friends decided to work together on the*

*story of how Rivers's family has grown and changed and how the little community
on the Bering Sea has changed as well. Rivers's mother, Mary Ann Sundown, also
contributed to the book by telling about the way people lived during the years she
grew up near Scammon Bay.*

HISTORY OF THE TUNRIT

traditional Netsilik Eskimo legend
translated by Edward Field
illustrated by Pudlo

When our forefathers came to these hunting grounds
the Tunrit people already lived here.
It was the Tunrit who first learned
how to survive in this difficult country.
They showed us the caribou crossing places
and taught us the special way to fish in the rivers.

Our people came from inland
so we love caribou hunting more than anything else,
but the Tunrit were sea people
and preferred to hunt seal.
They actually went out on the salt sea in their kayaks,
hunting seal in open water. That takes nerve.
We only hunt them through the ice at their breathing holes.
They also caught whales and walruses as they swam by:
The bones of these creatures are still lying around
in the wrecks of the Tunrit houses.
And they hunted bear and wore their skins for clothes.
We wear caribou.

The Tunrit were strong, but easily frightened.
In a fight they would rather run than kill. Anyway,
you never heard of them killing anyone.
And we lived among the Tunrit in those days peacefully,
for they let us come and share their land:
Until once by accident some of them killed one of our dogs
and ran away scared, leaving their homeland.

All of the Tunrit fled from their villages here finally,
although we cannot remember why anymore:
They just ran away or the land was taken from them.
And on leaving us they cried:
"We followed the caribou and hunted them down,
now it is your turn to follow them and do the hunting."

And so we do to this day.

THE NIGHT WE STARTED DANCING

Ann Cameron
illustrated by Gonzalez Vicente

I am named after my dad, Luis, but everybody calls me
Luisito. I live with my grandfather and grandmother; my
four uncles; my two aunts; my cousin, Diego; a girl named
Maria who helps my grandmother; our two dogs, Chubby and
Pilot; our two cats, Stripes and Hunter; and our big green parrot, Bright Star, that my grandmother always says she is going
to bake and serve for dinner someday.

We live in a town called Santa Cruz, in Guatemala, Central America. Santa Cruz has a park where there are great
band concerts, free, every week. It has a public school, and a
big college for army cadets, and it has an electronics store
where you could special-order a computer, but it doesn't have
paved streets, it has only dirt streets that turn to dust in the
winter when it's dry, and to mud in the summer when it rains.

I like dirt streets. It goes with the special thing about Santa
Cruz, which is that it's a very old town. It was a town before
Columbus discovered America, and before the Spaniards

came from Spain to steal our land and our gold and make slaves of people, because they said their religion was the true one, and God liked them better than us.

On the edge of Santa Cruz there is a high hill covered with old pine trees and the ruins of pyramids and an ancient fortress. That's where the headquarters of our people was, the headquarters of the kingdom of the Quichés, where our ancestors fought the Spaniards harder than anybody in Guatemala, before they lost for good.

Once, when I was six, a real Spaniard from Spain came to our house for dinner. He was going to do some business with my grandfather, so my grandmother invited him.

The whole dinner I kept watching my grandfather and the Spaniard all the time, and looking at my grandfather's big machete knife that he keeps by the front door.

Finally, I couldn't stand it, I said, "*Con permiso*, excuse me," and got up from the table and followed my grandmother into the kitchen when she went to get more food, and I even ducked under Bright Star's perch to get there faster.

"When?" I asked my grandmother. "When is he going to do it?"

"Who?" my grandmother said. "Do what?"

"When is Grandpa going to kill the Spaniard?" I whispered, and Bright Star hissed in his loudest voice, "Kill the Spaniard!" and the Spaniard looked around fast and dropped his fork.

My grandfather stopped munching his tortilla. "Don't be concerned," he said to the Spaniard, "we just have a crazy parrot," and my grandmother said, "One day I am going to bake you, Bright Star!"

Then she took me into one of the bedrooms and closed the door.

"What is this all about?" she said. "Why would Grandpa kill the Spaniard?"

"For being a Spaniard," I said.

"Are you crazy?" my grandmother said. "How can the Spaniard help being a Spaniard? He was born one, just like you were born a Guatemalan and a Quiché. Don't you know the battles with the Spaniards were over hundreds of years ago? We have to judge people by what they do, not by where they come from. And we have to fight our own battles, too, not the ones our ancestors fought."

So that was when I first found out that we'd never get our kingdom back—at least not the way it used to be.

My grandfather was born poor, and he never went to school. He worked from the time he was six years old, out in the wheat fields and the cornfields, hoeing. Every day when he finished work and went home, he would pass by his own dad in the street, drinking and spending all the family money. My great-granddad never helped my granddad at all. But my granddad just kept working, and when he was twenty, he started buying land—pieces nobody thought were good for anything—and on the land he planted apple orchards, and when the apples grew all over, big and beautiful, he got rich. He built a big house for my grandmother and our family, with five big bedrooms, and a patio in the middle full of flowers, and a living room where he and my grandmother put up all the pictures of both their families, except my grandfather never put up a picture of his dad. Then, last year, he must have finally started feeling sorry for his father, because he got his picture out of a drawer, and dusted it off, and put it up in the living room, only not with the rest of the pictures. So now my great-grandfather is staring out at the rest of the family, kind of ashamed-looking, from behind a fern.

My grandmother only learned to read four years ago, but she made my aunts and uncles study hard in school, and now she's making me do it, too. When I asked her why I had to study so hard, she said, "So that you aren't working with a hoe in the fields all your life, with the sun beating down on your head like a hammer."

When my grandparents' kids got to be old enough to study in the capital, my grandparents bought a house there for them to live in. So most of the year my aunts and uncles are there, studying architecture, and economics, and dentistry, and law, and accounting, and psychology. Only my youngest aunt, Celia, who is sixteen, is still living in Santa Cruz all the time. But next year she's going to the capital, too. She says she's going to study to be a doctor. My grandparents are very proud of all their children. The sad thing is, their oldest son, the only one who was studying agriculture and who loved the land the way my grandfather does, was my father, and he died. My mother died with him.

My mother was teaching grade school and my dad was in the last year of his agriculture studies when they died. I was four years old.

It happened four years ago, when my mom and dad and I and Uncle Ricardo were taking a bus from the capital to go back to my grandparents' house for Christmas. The bus terminal was full of dust and people trying to sell ice cream and coconuts and last-minute Christmas presents. Lots of people were going back to their hometowns for the holidays, and there weren't enough buses. Everybody was pushing and shoving to get on the ones there were.

My mom had a suitcase, and my dad had me on his back because he figured I couldn't run fast enough, and Uncle Ricardo was staring toward the sun with his hand shading his eyes, trying to see the bus that goes to Santa Cruz.

"Santa Cruz! That's it! Run!" he shouted, and my mom and dad raced for the front door of the bus, and Uncle Ricardo raced for the back, and they did flying dives over the top of a bunch of other people. My mom and dad got seats right behind the driver, and I sat on my mom's lap. Uncle Ricardo got stuck at the back, standing up.

Everybody pushed the windows down to get more air, and the driver put the bus in gear, but it didn't move, and his helper, the ticket taker, got out a hammer and a wrench and raised the hood on the bus and hammered on something for a while, and then the driver tried to move the bus again, and it went, and Uncle Ricardo heard my mother say, "A miracle! What a miraculous miracle!" and the ticket taker ran after the moving bus and jumped in the open door with the hammer and the wrench in his hand, and we were off.

Uncle Ricardo settled in and tried to take his elbow out of the stomach of the person on his right, and get his feet out from under the feet of the person on his left. My mom and dad were probably about the only ones who could see out the window, and who knew how the driver was driving.

The bus didn't go very fast, because it couldn't with so many people on it, but after a while Uncle Ricardo felt the bus lurch, and he heard my dad say to the driver, "Be careful, brother!" so he figured that the bus driver must have been taking a chance passing on a mountain curve.

A little while later he felt the bus twist again, and he heard my father say to the driver, "A man who foresees trouble and prevents it, is worth two men." But it seemed like the driver didn't feel like listening, because a little while later Uncle Ricardo heard my father say, "No matter where you are going, you don't have to get there first. The thing is, to get there."

And after that he heard my mother say, "Driver, there is more time than life."

And that was all he heard, except for my mother's voice just once more, shouting, "Luisito!" just before my father grabbed me with one hand and threw me out the window.

The bus driver went head-on into another bus. And my mother was right, because time just keeps going on and on and on, but she and my dad and the bus driver and the ticket taker and a lot of other people ran out of life completely.

Uncle Ricardo was okay because he was at the back, and I was okay.

The only part I remember begins with the grip of my father's hand, and how it hurt when he shoved me through the window frame. But I don't like to remember. I like to think about daytime things, my aunts and uncles, and things that are happening now.

But sometimes I still dream about it, being thrown out the window. In the dream I am little again, the same age I was then, and I land down a hillside in a freshly hoed field, just the way I really landed, but it is not daytime, it is almost completely dark, and I get up and go back to the wrecked bus, to find my mom and dad, but it gets darker and darker, and I never can find them.

Uncle Ricardo says one day I won't have the dream anymore. He says that my parents loved me a lot, and that I will always have them in my heart. He says one day my dream self will understand that, too. It will know that my parents are always with me when I remember them. It won't have to go back to the wrecked bus to look for them anymore.

And really I am okay, and Uncle Ricardo is okay, and my grandmother also is okay, because she loves all her children very much, but equally. The only one who has not been okay is my grandfather, because he loved my dad more than anybody. My dad wasn't only his son, he was his best friend.

The first Christmas after the accident we didn't celebrate, because nobody wanted to. But the next Christmas we didn't celebrate either, because Grandpa didn't want to. On the anniversary of the accident, he cut a lot of white roses and put them in front of my parents' wedding picture that hangs in the living room, and we visited their graves at the cemetery, so that was all there was of Christmas that year, too.

And from the beginning my grandmother said we shouldn't mention my mom and dad in front of my grandfather because it might upset him too much. She said we should just wait, and in time he would get better.

But it got to be September of the third year after my father died, and my grandfather still wasn't any better. My aunt Patricia, who had been leaving my cousin Diego with us a lot in Santa Cruz, decided to take Diego to the city. She said it was because she didn't have so many courses and she would have more time to spend with him, but Uncle Ricardo told me it was really because she thought it was too gloomy for Diego around our house.

The only reason I liked being in the house is that I like my grandmother and Celia a lot, my grandmother because she never yells at anybody, and Celia because she treats me like a grown-up. She got me to help her with a lot of projects, especially her Laugh Development Project, in which she said she needed the opinion of a man.

She wanted to develop four new laughs, even though my grandmother said it was a waste of time, and she couldn't see what was wrong with the laugh Celia was born with.

Celia said these are modern times, and a person should have five of everything. She said her original laugh was for when she really felt like laughing, and the other four would be for when she couldn't afford to be serious. She wanted my opinion because she wanted to make sure the four new laughs would be good enough to impress boyfriends.

So when Grandpa wasn't around, she practiced in front of the big cracked mirror on the patio.

"Ha, ha, HAH, HAH, hah," went the first laugh, which is a rapid one where she tosses her long black hair back behind her shoulders. That is her Rio de Janeiro laugh.

"Ho ho ho," she laughs slowly, and rubs her chin thoughtfully with the finger of one hand. That's her Paris laugh.

"Hee hee hee," she giggles, and covers her eyes with her hands. That's her Tahiti laugh.

"Hoo, hoo, hoo, hoo," she laughs, and raises her eyebrows very high. That's her Mexico City laugh.

She got all the ideas for the laughs from TV and from fashion magazines. After she got them all worked out, I told her they were all good, except the Tahiti laugh, which looked like she was just waking up in the morning, so she decided to rename it a waking-up laugh, to throw a stretch into it.

So she did. But just when she had them all perfect, Bright Star got them perfect, too. He sang them all off in a row, and then he said, in my voice, "Laugh Development Project."

"Now I can't bring any boyfriend home!" Celia said. "Either I can't bring one home, or I can't use my laughs."

"Not only that," I said, "Grandpa is going to know about this for sure."

Celia shrugged. "Maybe he'll borrow a laugh," she said. "He doesn't seem to have one of his own. Anyway, what more can he do? We already don't have Christmas anymore."

Sure enough, when Grandpa came home, Bright Star talked. He laughed all four laughs, and then imitated me, saying "Laugh Development Project."

It happened at dinner. My grandfather looked at Bright Star, and he looked at Celia, and he looked at me, but all he said was, "After school tomorrow, I want to take you out to the orchards, Luisito."

So I said okay, and the next afternoon we hiked out to the orchards.

"You are around your Aunt Celia too much," my grandfather said, but not unkindly. "You need the influence of a man."

"I am a man," I said.

"You are?" my grandfather said. "How do you know?"

"Celia said so."

He looked at me and said it took more than Celia's saying so to make somebody a man, and then he started telling me about the trees, and what you had to do to take care of them, and how many different kinds of apples there were, and how you could tell them apart.

But a bad thing happened, because the orchards are right next to the pyramids and the forts of the old kingdom, and I kept thinking about them and wanting to go over there, instead of listening to my grandfather.

"Luisito," he said suddenly, "how many kinds of apples do I have?"

And I couldn't tell him.

"You're not listening! Your father understood and remembered everything when he was your age!" he shouted. "Go on home to your grandmother!"

So I left, and instead of going straight home, I went over to the pyramids and ran up to the top of the biggest and stood there listening to the branches of the pine trees in the wind. It didn't help anything. And then I walked home alone.

When I told my grandma what happened, she said, "Your dad did understand and remember very well when he was your age. But when he was your age, he also played with matches once and set a whole cornfield on fire. It took us, the neighbors and the whole fire department to put it out."

"Tell Grandpa that!" I said. "Remind him about it!"

"I will sometime," my grandmother said, "but not now."

"When?" I asked. "You said Grandpa would get better and we just had to be patient. He used to make jokes, Celia says. He used to take everybody on trips. Now he never does, and he never gets any better."

"You are right," my grandmother said.

"Besides," I said, "Christmas is coming, and I am tired of not having Christmas, and so is Celia."

"You're probably right," my grandmother said. "We should celebrate Christmas."

And she actually used the telephone, which she never uses, to call up Ricardo and talk to him about it.

And that night at dinner, she told my grandfather, "It's time we started to celebrate Christmas again."

"I would rather not," my grandfather said.

"The children say they won't come home for Christmas, unless we celebrate, like the old days. Luis and Celia say they would rather go into the city to be with Ricardo and everybody if we don't celebrate Christmas."

"Um," my grandfather said.

"I might go, too," my grandmother said.

"*You* might go?" my grandfather said.

"Yes, I probably will go," my grandmother said.

"You would *leave* me?" my grandfather said.

"Just for Christmas," my grandmother said.

"It wouldn't be good," my grandfather said. "We've been together thirty-one years. You've never been away. Not one day!"

"Times change," my grandmother said.

"Well," my grandfather said, "we had better celebrate Christmas. But I won't dance."

"You don't have to dance," my grandmother said. "Nobody has to dance. But at least we will have dance music, anyway."

Celia and I made a beautiful golden Christmas tree out of corn husks that we cut to fasten on wires and make the shape of branches. When we were done, the tree went all the way to the ceiling, and we draped it with red chains of tinsel. And my grandmother stood in front of the stove all Christmas Eve day making the tamales for the midnight dinner—corn stuffed with chicken and meat and olives and raisins and hot chili sauce, and wrapped in banana leaves to cook. And everybody arrived from the city about six-thirty at night, just in time for the supper we were going to have to tide us over to the real dinner at midnight.

Uncle Ricardo brought Diego and me about sixty firecrackers to set off at midnight, when all the kids in town go outside to set off firecrackers, so we were feeling good. And my grandfather had dressed up in his best and happiest clothes, new pants, and a cap that makes him look as young as my uncles.

Everybody hugged, and we all sat down to eat, but nobody talked much until we were almost finished, when Aunt Patricia said, "All the same, it's sad anyway."

And my Uncle Pedro, who had been an exchange student in the U.S. for one year of high school, said, "If the roads had shoulders, the way the highways do in the U.S., they never would have died."

And Celia said, "So in the great U.S.A. there are no traffic accidents?"

And before Pedro could answer her, my grandfather got up out of his chair and went out on the patio, and we all stopped talking.

"Luisito," my grandmother said, "go be with your grandfather."

So I went out on the patio and stood by my grandfather, who was looking up at the sky and wouldn't look down.

I just stood there by him, looking up, too.

There was a full moon, shining down on the patio and on the papery violet leaves of the bougainvillea, and my grandfather spoke, in a choked voice.

"See the leaves? There are so many you can't see the branch, and all different.

"And we are like them, all different, but holding on to an invisible branch—but two of us are missing!

"Why do they have to talk about it? Don't they know I've cried enough? What do they think I do out in the orchard, but cry?"

"You should cry with us," I said, and I saw my grandfather's eyes drop tears, and we stood there a long time.

Everybody else had gone into the living room, and while we were standing there, the dance music started, very slowly, low music, soft like smoke, winding into the moonlight.

"Oh, Luisito," my grandfather said. "What can we do? What can anybody do? Luisito, we should dance."

And so my granddad and I danced, around the cage of Bright Star, who was sleeping under a new Christmas blanket, and past the cracked mirror and the bougainvillea vine, and then, very slowly, into the living room. And then I danced with Celia, and my grandfather put his arms around my grandmother and danced with her, and everybody danced with everybody, straight through until midnight when the fireworks started going off in huge booms all over town, and we all held hands, and everyone of us kissed every other one, and I noticed for the first time in a long time that in the photo of my mom and dad, above Grandpa's white roses, they were smiling.

THE WEST SIDE

from HOW JUAN GOT HOME
by Peggy Mann
illustrated by Karin Lidbeck

*Juan Morales has come from Puerto Rico
to New York to live with his Uncle Esteban. Juan's mother
believes that he will receive a better education in New York than
in Puerto Rico. When the plane lands and his uncle's arrival at
the airport is delayed, Juan is told that the airline will give him a
free flight back to Puerto Rico if his uncle does not arrive to pick
him up. Juan misunderstands and believes he will be able to
return to Puerto Rico any time he decides to do so. After a few
days in his uncle's apartment and some unsuccessful attempts to
make friends with the English-speaking boys who live on his
street, Juan is unhappy and is determined to return to Puerto
Rico. In the meantime, however, he agrees to go on a shopping
expedition for Puerto Rican food in a neighborhood on the
West Side of New York.*

Juan stepped off the bus at Columbus Avenue. It was as
though he had stepped off the bus into Puerto Rico. The
street was alive with children and Spanish music. Some of
the children, barefoot and wet, played around the water gush-
ing from a fire hydrant, ran in and out screaming laughter and
Spanish words. Latin music came blaring from radios on win-
dowsills . . . from a young man who sat on a box in front of
Bodega Rivera strumming a guitar and singing a Spanish love

song . . . from a bongo band on the corner playing hard rock with a loud Latin beat.

Women leaned out of windows shrilling in Spanish to children on the street. A group of men sat around a bridge table on the sidewalk, playing dominoes. Women in bright cotton dresses sat on the front steps gossiping in Spanish. And the stores! At home the stores often had *americano* names: the Blue Moon Bar Restaurant . . . Joe's Shop . . . the Cooperative . . . Mercado's Barbershop . . . But here: everything Spanish! Farmacia Flores . . . Tienda La Favorita . . . Zapatería El Quijote . . . Repostería Borinquén. . . .

All crowded together like this, the store signs, the music, the look and the sound of the Spanish people, it seemed somehow *more* Puerto Rican than anything he had seen in Puerto Rico. He was no longer a stranger. He didn't even need to ask directions. With a smile on his face he strode into Bodega Rivera.

He *was* home. The small crowded grocery store was just like the one on his street in Barranquitas. The same small, sweet *niños* bananas hung in clumps in the dusty window; and the long, green *plátanos* hung next to them on iron hooks. The same bins of tropical fruits and vegetables. The same cans and bottles on the shelves: guava juice, papaya juice, *asopao de jueyes*, red beans, pink beans, white beans, pinto beans, chick peas, *Doraditos*, *Florecitas*, *coco rico* and *chinita*. Even the same penny candy machine. And the same packets of ladies' panty hose on the rack behind the counter.

The shopkeeper, who wore a large black mustache and a dirty white apron, was arguing with a customer about the price of his *batatas*. Loudly Señor Rivera informed her that he had to import the *batatas* from the island. If she could not pay for special Spanish food she should eat American.

When, grumbling, she counted out her money, and left, a boy about Juan's age stood on tiptoe in front of the counter and asked in a loud voice whether Señor Rivera would sell him some boxes.

"Boxes of *what?*" Señor Rivera said.

"Empty boxes," the boy said. "We're having a stickball game on the street tomorrow afternoon and we already sold twenty box seats to people who want to watch from the sidewalk. Now we gotta get the boxes."

"Get out of here, Carlos," Señor Rivera said. "I'm busy."

"But Señor Rivera!" Carlos persisted. "I'm willing to pay for the boxes. Usually you give them out free to customers. I'm going to *pay!*"

"Yes?" Señor Rivera said. "And how are my customers going to carry home their groceries if I got no more boxes?"

"Listen," Carlos said, "I'll make you a deal. If you let us have the boxes, I'll let your son Willie umpire the game."

Señor Rivera said nothing. He scowled.

"As you know," Carlos said, "your boy Willie is kind of a pain-in-the-neck kid. That's why he gets beat up so much. But nobody beats up an umpire. You got to respect an umpire."

"How much did you sell the box seats for?" said Señor Rivera.

"Five cents a box for cardboard, ten cents for wood. I told them they could take the seats home with them."

"And how much are you planning to pay me, Carlos, for every box I give you?"

"Well," Carlos said, "a penny for cardboard. Two cents for wood."

Señor Rivera laughed. "Carlos," he said, "you're going to grow up to be the president of the First National Bank. Listen," he added, "go down in my cellar and haul yourself up twenty boxes. You can have them for free."

Carlos grinned and started for the flight of steps leading down to the cellar.

"Save a box seat for me," Señor Rivera called after him. "I want to come watch my son Willie be umpire."

Juan then stood on tiptoe in front of the greasy glass counter. He ordered twelve *plátanos verdes*, two pounds of *gandules* and one ounce of *ajíes*. But when he paid his money, and held the three paper bags in his hands, he still did not want to leave.

If only his uncle had the job of maintenance engineer on Columbus Avenue! Then he, Juan, might not even want to go home. If he lived over here, then he could go to school over here. Maybe here they even had Spanish schools and he'd never need to learn English at all!

But Uncle Esteban had explained that a boy must go to school in the district where he lived. He would have to go to school on the rich East Side of Manhattan; a school which would, no doubt, be filled up tight with *americanos*.

He noticed the boy called Carlos who came staggering up from the cellar with an armload of cardboard boxes. "Hey!" He walked over to Carlos. "You want me to help you carry those boxes to wherever you're going?"

"Sure," Carlos said in English. "Matter of fact, I was going to ask you to give me a hand." He smiled.

Juan didn't understand the English, but a smile was the same in any language.

He smiled back.

They made two trips from the Bodega Rivera to the basement of the brownstone rooming house where Carlos lived. Juan kept talking almost nonstop all the way. He had so much talk inside him it seemed he just couldn't get it all said.

Carlos spoke very little. When they had finished piling the boxes in a corner of the basement, Carlos explained why he always answered Juan in such short sentences. He knew very little Spanish.

Juan stared at him through the basement gloom, astounded. A *puertorriqueño* who didn't know Spanish?

Carlos shrugged and explained that they'd come from the mainland when he was three years old to live with his grandmother. He'd been brought up on English, in the streets and in school. In fact, the only Spanish he knew came from talking to his grandmother.

Juan nodded. He felt he had found a friend—only to lose him. What was worse, he felt like a fool. Here he'd been jabbering away to this boy all about Barranquitas and his house and his mother and sisters and friends and his miniature car collection and the Piñonas River and his school and the TV programs he watched at home. And all the time Carlos had hardly understood a single word!

"As a matter of fact," Carlos said in English as he started up the basement stairs, "you'll find that most of the Spanish kids on this street don't speak Spanish. At least, their Spanish is nothing to speak of!" Then, having made a kind of pun, Carlos laughed.

But Juan trudging up the stairs behind him did not laugh. He had not understood a word Carlos said.

Carlos turned then and repeated the sentences in a stiff and inaccurate Spanish.

Juan nodded glumly. He felt betrayed. Even if he took the bus over here every day to play with the *puertorriqueño* kids on Columbus Avenue, it would be no good. He would still be a stranger—among his own people. Only they weren't his own people anymore. They were *americanos*.

When they reached the street Carlos said, in Spanish, "Well, thanks for helping me out."

And, in Spanish, Juan replied. "That's okay." Then he added, "I better say good-bye now. I'll be going back home at the end of the week."

"To the island?" Carlos said, in some surprise.

Juan nodded.

"You must be pretty rich," Carlos said, "to come hopping all the way over here just for one week. How much is the plane fare?"

Juan explained that the trip home wouldn't cost him anything. The airline would fly him home free.

Carlos frowned. He did not understand. "Free? How could that be?"

Juan, speaking in slow careful Spanish as though he were addressing a very small child, explained how the airline had promised to send him home free the night he arrived. So since he hadn't taken them up on their offer then, he would do so at the end of the week.

"Listen, you stupid kid," Carlos said. "Sure they were going to send you home free when your uncle didn't show up. I mean they can't let a little kid like you just be hanging around the airport at night all alone. But your uncle *did* show up. So the offer's over. Now you're *his* worry. Not theirs. How could they ever make any money if they kept dealing out free tickets to anyone wanting to make a trip back home?"

He spoke now in English. Juan kept nodding. Then he said, "*No entiendo*. I not onnerstan'."

So, with some effort, Carlos repeated it all in Spanish. Juan nodded again. This time he understood all too well, and knew with certainty that Carlos was correct. In fact, this very thought had been lurking in the back of his mind. But he hadn't allowed it to come forward before. Because he didn't want to know the truth. The truth that he *could* not go home.

"Listen, kid," Carlos said suddenly, in Spanish, "since you helped me with the boxes, how'd you like a free box seat for the game tomorrow afternoon?"

"What kind of game?" Juan asked.

"Stickball."

"What's stickball?"

"Stickball's what it says it is," Carlos said. "You hit a ball with a stick. Want me to show you?"

Juan nodded.

"C'mon," Carlos said. "I got my equipment upstairs." He shoved open the front door and Juan followed him into the hallway. The place smelled strongly of cats and rancid cooking oil and the garbage which sat outside each doorway in overflowing pails or paper bags.

Juan felt like holding his breath and holding his nose. Who would want to live in such a place when they could be back in the fresh mountain air of Barranquitas where the only smell one noticed was that of flowers?

When they reached the third floor Carlos took a ring of keys from his pocket and started unlocking one of the doors. "We got three different locks," he explained to Juan, "because we have been robbed five times."

Juan was impressed. Carlos must live in a pretty big place with some valuable things in it for anyone to bother robbing his apartment five times. After all, even though the hallways smelled, that didn't mean the apartments weren't beautiful inside.

But inside there was nothing much either. Just one room with a flowered curtain drawn across the middle. The whole place was not much bigger than the bedroom he shared at home with his two sisters. There was a wooden table and four wooden chairs all painted bright green. There was a picture of the Virgin Mary tacked to the wall. And in the corner a small stove and large sink, stacked with dishes. Sunlight fell in through the open window and lay in a long oblong pattern across the worn green linoleum on the floor. There was a flower box on the windowsill with some geraniums in it.

Not a bad place, Juan thought. At least it looked friendly. He'd a lot rather live here than in Uncle Esteban's fine basement apartment where all the windows had bars like a jail.

Carlos meanwhile had gone behind the curtain. He came back with a small rubber ball and a broom. "Of course," he said, "the bat we play with is a mop handle without the mop. But our captain keeps that in his house. I'm the manager of

the team," he added, with an edge of pride in his voice. "That means I set up the games and arrange everything. The big game we got on tomorrow is against the Young Princes. Come on. I'll show you how we play."

Juan followed Carlos into the hallway again, waited while his new friend locked the door with three different keys, and went down the stairs after him, taking two at a time as Carlos did.

In the street Carlos waited until a few cars had gone by. Then, when there was a lull in the traffic, he stepped out, threw the ball into the air, swung the broom handle hard. And missed.

Shamefaced, he picked up the ball. "Well, I myself am not so hot at this game," he said in English. "I'm better at organizing than playing. But the idea is, if you hit the ball past the first sewer that's pretty good. If you hit it past the second sewer, that's sensational. And if you hit it past the third sewer, that's impossible. The third sewer's right down at the end of the street. You can hardly even see it from here."

Juan nodded. He had barely understood a word that Carlos said. But he was embarrassed to ask his friend to repeat it all over again in Spanish. So he asked instead, "I try?"

"Sure," Carlos said and threw him the broom which Juan caught in one hand. Then Carlos threw the ball which Juan caught in the other hand. And stepped out into the street.

"Hey! *Watch it!*" Carlos screamed in English.

Juan stepped back just as a yellow taxi sped by his toes. He'd been so intent about showing Carlos that he could hit this ball with the broom that he forgot about everything else—including getting run over. His heart now started thudding with fear at his narrow escape.

"Listen!" Carlos said sternly. "They got such things as cars in this city and don't you ever forget that!"

Juan nodded. He looked carefully up and down the street.

"It's okay now," Carlos said. "Nothing coming."

But still Juan felt afraid.

"Hurry up! *Avanza!*" Carlos said. "Take your chance while you got it."

So Juan, his heart still pounding, stepped out into the street, threw the rubber ball into the air, and hit it with the broom handle. Hard.

He watched the ball proudly as it sped through the air.

Carlos screamed again. And again Juan rushed back to the safety of the sidewalk. But this time there were no cars coming. This time Carlos screamed for another reason. "You hit

three sewers!" he kept screaming. "Man, don't you understand, you hit *three sewers!*"

"Yes," said Juan. "I onnerstan'." He did not know what "three sewers" meant. But he did understand that Carlos was impressed at how he had hit the ball.

"Listen," Carlos said. "You must be puttin' me on, man. Telling me you never played stickball before." He repeated the question in Spanish. The words were charged with suspicion. "You sure you never played stickball before?"

Juan shook his head. "No," he said. "I have never played stickball before." He saw no reason to explain that he had been playing stick-stone ever since he was seven years old. Hitting a stone with a stick across the Piñonas River in the Contest game he had invented.

"Listen, kid," Carlos said suddenly. "How'd you like to play on our team tomorrow afternoon?" Then, slowly, carefully he tried the words in Spanish. "*¿Vas a jugar con nosotros mañana?*"

Juan grinned. "Sure, man," he said in English. "Hokay!"

CHINATOWN

from CHILD OF THE OWL by Laurence Yep
illustrated by Yoriko Ito

*In the time since her mother, Jeanie, died, Casey Young
has traveled around California with her father, Barney. But
when he becomes sick and has to be hospitalized, Casey goes to
live with her grandmother, Paw-Paw, in San Francisco's
Chinatown. Here she begins to learn more about her Chinese
heritage and about her mother.*

I lay in bed thinking for a long time after Paw-Paw had finished her story. I'd never asked her about Jeanie before
this, I suppose, because Barney had taught me not to talk
about her. Finally I rolled over on my side to face her. "When
did Jeanie feel lonely?"

Paw-Paw picked up a deck of cards and began to play a
game of solitaire. She could play even while she talked. A
three on the four of one column. A jack on the queen of
another column. Flip. Flip. Flip. Like her fingers had eyes and
brains so Paw-Paw didn't even have to look down. Her hands
could do everything. "Maybe I should let your daddy tell you."

I turned so I lay on my stomach, hugging a pillow under my
chin. "Barney won't talk much about her. Was she lonely
when she was my age?"

Paw-Paw must have sensed the longing in my voice. "Oh, no. Your mommy always had lots of friends. She was very pretty. And very sweet. She was always a big help to me." Paw-Paw finished her game and began to sweep the cards into the middle of the table so she could gather them into a deck. "And your daddy was thought to be a very good-looking boy so they were always a natural couple. From grammar school on."

"Grammar school?"

"They both went to Commodore Stockton just a little way from here. And then they went through junior high and high school together." Paw-Paw began to shuffle her cards to get them ready for the next time she wanted to play.

"Were they very popular?"

"Oh, yes. Very popular. You'd always see them together at all the dances in Chinatown. Your momma liked dancing."

Paw-Paw went to the bureau and opened a middle drawer, rummaging around till she took out an old, worn brown bag and drew a small pile of photos out of it. She set them down on the table and sorted through them. "That's your momma. She was going to a dance that night." Paw-Paw tapped one photo of a pretty girl of about sixteen in bobby sox and a long skirt like all the American girls used to wear—or at least that's

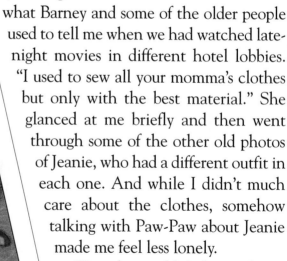

what Barney and some of the older people used to tell me when we had watched late-night movies in different hotel lobbies. "I used to sew all your momma's clothes but only with the best material." She glanced at me briefly and then went through some of the other old photos of Jeanie, who had a different outfit in each one. And while I didn't much care about the clothes, somehow talking with Paw-Paw about Jeanie made me feel less lonely.

"But she couldn't have always gone out with Barney. What did she do with you for fun? I mean, besides playing cards."

"We went to see Chinese movies." Paw-Paw put her cards down in a neat stack by the little cup that held her toothpicks. They were cinnamon-flavored and each was wrapped in a little paper envelope. "Would you like to see a movie like your mommy and I used to see?"

I wasn't doing much of anything so I figured why not. "I've got money for myself."

"Why spend your money? I can sew some extra shirts this week."

"Are you sure it's okay?" I asked.

"Of course, it's okay," she snapped and I could see there would be no arguing with her.

Paw-Paw bundled up as usual, putting on a blouse over her pajama top and then a sweater and a heavy silk jacket over the sweater so that by the time she had on her heavy cloth coat, she looked twice as round. Over her head she put her favorite vermilion chiffon scarf with the roses embroidered on it with gold thread.

Paw-Paw seemed very comfortable within the small world of Chinatown; I wondered if Jeanie had been too. It didn't cover more than half a square mile or so then, and within those boundaries, as I was to find out, it is a very small, tightly knit world where everyone knows your business and you know theirs. To the west lay the souvenir shops and on the east, delicatessens and grocery stores and meat markets, some of which had fish tanks in the bottom half of their windows in which a hundred fish would be squeezed, all staring out at you with cold, black eyes, or even turtles, or sometimes cages of snakes, all to be sold and eaten.

To the north was Stockton Street, where my school was. Mostly it was sewing-machine shops up that way: plain storefronts sometimes with wallpaper covering the windows or old, sun-bleached curtains. From within would come the steady whir and whine of the machines of the ladies sewing dresses, shirts, even jeans and expensive wedding outfits for American stores. A lot of ladies with no English could only do that. Just above Stockton Street was the public grammar school, Commodore Stockton, or "Commodore" to the kids. Across from it lay the YWCA and Cameron House, a kind of club for Chinese kids. Above that, where Paw-Paw never went, were the cable-car lines and the apartment houses for Americans, including the fancy hotels and limousines of Nob Hill.

But at that moment I was thinking mainly about the movies we were going to see. I had my doubts because all I had seen up to then were Charlie Chan movies or silly houseboys on TV shows or funny laundrymen in westerns. But even so, one of those kinds of movies was better than nothing because I knew Paw-Paw never left Chinatown to see any of the Hollywood movies just a few blocks away.

We went to the Chinese Globe that had a bright neon sign outside in front and looked like a regular theater except for the fact that there was a guy selling newspapers by the ticket booth. He had about a dozen different Chinese newspapers laid in neat piles on a board that he laid over some boxes. But I saw a dozen portable newsstands like that set up all over Chinatown—in doorways or in corners or in front of busy stores. He nodded familiarly to Paw-Paw as she bought our tickets at the booth.

When I finally got to see the movies, they were completely different than I thought. I could see why Jeanie had liked them. For one thing, the Chinese were actually people who could be brave or sad. They had subtitles in English, too, which was good. It was something to see Chinese do more than be the sidekick to some white guy in a fight, or see the Chinese actually win. I mean, I almost felt like crying when I saw it: a kind of bubbling feeling deep down inside that had me almost cheering and crying while this Chinese mother led her three sons in beating up the bad guys. And it was even better when I saw the Chinese girls fighting.

The second feature, you see, was *Princess of the Streets*, which is about this girl who grows up in the back streets of Hong Kong. She gets friendly with this other girl who does juggling and fighting displays in a medicine show. And together she and her friend wipe out the big crime boss. I don't think I ever saw anyone jump as high in the air to kick someone.

It must have rained while we were inside the theater because when we came out later, the streets were slick and black, like they were made of shining crystal. I saw a Chinatown I'd never seen before. It was the Chinatown Jeanie must have seen. Suddenly all the gaudy neon signs were no longer a bunch of words but were like snakes of colored lights crawling up the faces of the buildings and their reflections smashed themselves on the streets, looking like broken stars sliding back and forth and trying to put themselves back together. Funny, but it seemed, right then, like I'd just come home.

A radio store had begun playing music over an outside loudspeaker. Some of the stuff, especially the opera, sounded terrible to me—a high whiny kind of noise—but this sounded different. Some people might have thought there was too much of a clutter of sound with the cymbals crashing and the drums beating and everybody playing like mad, but there was something inside of me that liked it—like it synchronized right with the pulsing of my blood through my body. And the sound wound its way through the chatter of the night-time crowds.

Humming with the tune, Paw-Paw took my arm for support as we made our way along the slippery pavements of Grant Avenue. We passed by the delicatessens, where Paw-Paw pointed to the dark-brown, roasted ducks dangling from hooks in the windows. "That's what I like," she said. "Jeanie too."

"I've never had duck in my life," I said.

She patted my arm, the one she was holding on to. "Maybe I'll sew some extra shirts and dresses someday and we'll buy half of one so you can try it."

We went about two blocks before the rain started to fall again. It was falling pretty hard so we stopped under the awning of this one souvenir shop. Paw-Paw acted like the window display had been put there just to entertain us. "Look at that whirly thing." She pointed at one of those little solar windmills that rotate whenever they're near a source of light like the light bulb illuminating the window.

There was something wrong about the window. At first I couldn't figure it out but as Paw-Paw went on mentioning things in the window, I realized she hadn't talked about one Chinese thing yet. I started to study the window then. There didn't seem to be anything as beautiful or as old as the owl charm Paw-Paw wore about her neck. There was just a lot of silly stuff like two-headed back-scratchers. Paw-Paw didn't point at any of those or at some of the things that were downright nasty—like pellet guns and various types of knives, from simple pocket- and hunting knives to switchblades and gravity blades that snap out with a flick of a wrist. The only thing vaguely Oriental that I saw at first in the window were the Japanese kimonos and geisha dolls they sold.

"It doesn't seem right somehow," I said. "I mean, if it's a Chinatown souvenir shop, shouldn't it be selling Chinese stuff?"

"The Americans won't let us bring in things from China." She shrugged. "And the Taiwan government's too busy to bother with souvenirs. You have to sell the Americans something."

"But we're selling things as if they're Chinese when it's really . . . well, I don't know . . . this stuff just seems like junk compared to your owl charm. There's no story behind most of this stuff. There's no meaning to this stuff. This junk is probably not even much fun."

"They do have a few real Chinese things. See?" She moved a little to the side and bent down, pointing to one dark corner of the window. "See down there in the back?"

I leaned forward slightly and looked where her finger was pointing and saw a bunch of dusty statues crowded together like they were making a last stand. "They've got some of the stuff you've got on your bureau. Look, there's that pretty lady with the flower."

Paw-Paw studied me. I hadn't laughed about the owl story and I had even liked the Chinese movies so I guess she decided to go ahead. "That lady is the Listener. She could have gone to heaven, but when she was just about to enter the gate, she could hear all the poor souls back on earth groaning and she turned her back on heaven, saying she could not enter until everyone else had gone before her, so she spends all her time trying to help the rest of us to heaven."

Though it was a cold, rainy night outside, I felt warm inside now that Paw-Paw was finally explaining things to me. "Hey, there's the guy with the big head."

"He's the spirit of long life," Paw-Paw corrected me. "His head swelled up because he's so full of life. He helps keep the record of your life and sometimes with special people he juggles his books and they live longer, so maybe someone dies when they're ninety-one instead of nineteen. He's got a magic peach in his hand, grown in heaven for the gods. A person eats that peach and that person lives forever."

And she told me the eight statues—not as small as hers—were the Eight Immortals who had once been simple men and women but had gained the secret of immortality. One of them had meditated so long and let his dream-soul wander so far away that his body died in the meantime and his dream-soul had to take the bony body of a crippled beggar when it got back.

She told me about a few more of the statues and when she stopped, I asked her a new question I'd been thinking about. "What would it be like if we were in China, Paw-Paw?"

Paw-Paw shut her eyes but kept her face turned toward the window as if she were trying to picture it herself. "It'd be very noisy and you'd have much less time to yourself than here. You have to go through the rain to the village lavatory. Or maybe you have to empty out a . . . a . . . what is the word? . . . a chamber pot."

"Ugh."

"No heat except the stuff in the stove so you have to go and look for every leaf and every bit of grass and all your neighbors would be doing the same thing."

"Would you have a whole bunch of families together in the same big house? Like Uncle Phil and Uncle Chester would live with you?" Uncle Chester was a year younger than Jeanie and lived down in L.A.

Paw-Paw shook her head. "Only if we were rich, but we'd probably be poor farmers if we had stayed back in China. Each of them would have their own little house and you and I would be crowded in somehow into one of those two."

I drew my finger down the glass slowly. Rain dribbled down from the awning overhead. "But still, would you like that better than the way you live now? I mean if we were in China, you'd really be in charge, like the mother was in the first movie, bossing all her grown-up sons around."

Paw-Paw sighed. "I don't know. It's too easy to worry about the way things might have been. I'd rather live with the way things are now. That's what the Owl Spirit did after all."

"Well, why don't you live with one of your children now?"

"I could live with your Uncle Phil anytime I want, but they always get this rotten chicken meat from the freezer, when chickens should be fresh. But no, the feathers make too much mess and they don't like it when I take out the blood and guts. And I say, 'What do you think's inside of you?' Or they give me steak in a huge chunk and they hand me a knife and that thing with the four sharp points."

"A fork?"

"Yes, and I say, 'When I come to the dinner table, I come to eat, not to cook. Meat should be cut up and cooked properly in the kitchen before dinner.' "

"They'd probably let you make your own meals," I said.

"Well, I guess I could make my peace with them on that, but there are other things." Her eyes glanced at the statues in the window. "They tell me those things are only for stupid, old people."

I realized that it all depended on how I looked around myself—if there were invisible walls around Chinatown for Paw-Paw, they were like the walls of a turtle, walls behind which you could remain warm and alive, and for someone like me, those walls didn't have to be any more of a trap than I let them. They could be like something to give me shape and form and when I couldn't grow anymore inside them, I could break out of those invisible walls.

Paw-Paw began to retie her scarf but her fingers had begun to stiffen in the cold and the wet. I reached my hands out. "Here, Paw-Paw, let me help you." So Paw-Paw leaned forward, waiting patiently until I had retied her scarf. She checked the knot under the chin of her reflection in the window, smoothing her hand over it.

She smiled, pleased. "You did that very well. Such strong young fingers."

She gripped my fingers tightly in her hand for a moment with what seemed like an immense strength. "Now help an old lady up the hills. It's wet and I'm afraid I'm going to fall."

I let her take my arm then and once again she was just a little old lady and we climbed slowly up the steeply slanting hillside, like two small owls clawing their way along a branch that twisted upward into the night sky.

MEET LAURENCE YEP, AUTHOR

Laurence Yep was born in San Francisco in 1948. Yep's father had come from China as a small boy, and his mother was born in West Virginia. It was his mother's mother, Marie Lee, who was the model for Paw-Paw in Child of the Owl. *In his autobiography,* The Lost Garden, *Yep explains that, like Casey Young, he grew up speaking English and eating with a fork. He says of his grandmother: "She represented a 'Chineseness' in my life that was as unmovable and unwanted as a mountain in your living room. . . . So there I was with all of these strange, new pieces [of my background] that my grandmother had presented to me; pieces that had to be put into the puzzle that was myself but no clue where those pieces were to go.*

"In part, to come up with some answers, I began to keep a file of family history. Whenever my mother, my aunts, or my grandmother told family stories, I would try to remember them so I could write them down later. It was only years later when I began to piece things together that I began to understand just how difficult a journey it had been for my grandmother from China, through Ohio and West Virginia and finally to her little home in Chinatown.

"More than anyone, I respected my grandmother. She had not only survived, but she had become her own person—which was something I wanted to do."

WOMEN

Alice Walker
illustrated by Tyrone Geter

They were women then
My mama's generation
Husky of voice—Stout of
Step
With fists as well as
Hands
How they battered down
Doors
And ironed
Starched white
Shirts
How they led
Armies
Headragged Generals
Across mined
Fields
Booby-trapped
Ditches
To discover books
Desks
A place for us
How they knew what we
Must know
Without knowing a page
Of it
Themselves.

MEET ALICE WALKER, POET

Alice Walker was born in Georgia in 1944, the eighth child
of a sharecropper and a maid. She says about her mother:
"She seemed a large, soft, loving-eyed woman who was
rarely impatient in our home. Her quick, violent temper was
on view only a few times a year, when she battled with the
white landlord, who had the misfortune to suggest to her that
her children did not need to go to school."

During her high school years, Walker's mother gave her three
gifts that Walker believes showed her mother's wishes for her.
The first was a sewing machine so that Walker could make
her own clothes. "I even made my own prom dress, such as it was, something
chartreuse net, I think. But the message about independence and self-sufficiency
was clear." The second was a suitcase: "That suitcase gave me permission to travel
and part of the joy in going very far from home was the message of that suitcase."
The third was a typewriter. "Oh yes, she bought me a typewriter when I was in
high school. How did my mama ever get that typewriter? She must have ordered it
from Sears. A typewriter and a little typewriter table. She did all this on less than
twenty dollars a week."

Italian immigrants seeking lost luggage. 1904. Lewis Hine.

Silver gelatin print. Dorothy Norman Collection, Philadelphia Museum of Art

Detail of a Japanese scroll
depicting an Ainu family.

18th century. Woodblock print. Private collection.
Photo: Werner Forman Archive/Art Resource

FINE ART
FAMILY HERITAGE

Family Greeting. 1962. Eli Tikeayak,
Canadian Inuit, Rankin Inlet.

Light green-grey stone. Gift of Robert C.
Williamson, C.M., Art Gallery of Ontario,
Toronto. © Kissarvik Co-op Association Ltd.

THE NIGHT JOURNEY

from the book by Kathryn Lasky
illustrated by Trina Schart Hyman

Rache lives with her parents, Ed and Leah; her grandmother, Rose; and her great-grandmother, Sashie. Rache's parents and grandmother warn her not to upset Nana Sashie by asking about tsarist Russia and the persecution Jewish people were subjected to there. However, Rache is fascinated by the story Nana Sashie has begun to tell about her family's dangerous escape from that country.

In an old trunk Rache finds a piece of the brass samovar, or tea urn, that figures largely in Nana Sashie's story. The samovar was the one thing that Sashie's mother, Ida, chose to take with her from Russia. The selection begins on the evening when Rache's father surprises the family with a rebuilt samovar. That night, Nana Sashie continues her story for Rache after the others have gone to bed.

"I have one last gift," said Ed.

"Oh, Ed, enough already!"

"This is actually a gift for the whole family."

"Ooooooh!" Rache, Leah, and the nanas exclaimed in unison.

"Just one minute while I get it." Ed went to the pantry and returned with something large and fairly tall wrapped in cloth. "It was too big to wrap in paper so I just put this cloth around it." As he set it on the table he asked, "Who wants to unwrap it?"

Rache was puzzled. There were not the usual hesitations, the if-you-don't-like-it statements.

"Rache, why don't you unwrap it?"

"Well, okay," said Rache with slight apprehension. She leaned forwards and gave a light tug. The cloth fell off. There was a sharp gusty sound as each of the women sucked in her breath in shock. Then silence. A samovar—polished and bright—stood before them. Rache heard Nana Sashie whisper something in Yiddish. The top piece—the crown, Ida's crown—flickered unquenchably in the candlelight. The good soldier was back! Rache sat stunned as conversation bubbled up around her.

"It's a samovar!"

Even the babies liked a glass of tea from the samovar.

"Ed, however did you do it?"

From my bed I could see the samovar.

"Well, the part that Rache found started me off."

"Were you here that day?"

Like a polished good soldier.

The words floated back to Rache through the din.

"So I started hunting in antique shops and got some leads from the museum—you know, just to find the other brass parts."

Its brass catching the glow of the gas lamp in the street outside.

"I'll tell you who was really incredibly helpful and who did most of the rebuilding when we got the parts was . . ."

I used to pretend it was a good soldier . . .

"Bo Andersen of Andersen's Jewelry. You know, the son, the kid . . ."

"You mean the one who's about forty?"

"Yes. Well, he just loved working on this."

"Nana Sashie?" Leah suddenly looked worried. "Ed, I hope this doesn't . . . Nana Sashie, are you all right?"

A sentry in the darkness standing watch over us.

There were two small pockets of loud silence in the happy din—one was Nana Sashie, whose face seemed lost in a gentle reverie, and the other was Rache, who, now over her initial astonishment, felt a confusing mixture of emotions. When she had first discovered the samovar part, Rache had been disgusted by Leah's and Nana Rose's ignorance of Sashie's Russia. But now she felt a real apprehension, as if the gulf between the two worlds had closed too quickly and the one world that she had explored with Sashie would no longer be just theirs alone. Sashie! Funny, she had never thought of her as just Sashie before. She had always been Nana Sashie. It was odd. Odder still was her father. Did he know about the meetings with Nana Sashie? Had he seen her go into Nana's room that night?

"Rache! Come back to the world of the living. Thank you."

"Oh, sorry!"

"Nana Sashie asked you a question."

"Oh! What? What Nana?"

"Would you kindly fetch the toolbox. There are a few bolts that need tightening if we are going to use this for making tea—which we are!"

After tightening several bolts, Nana Sashie declared the samovar fit for a trial run and insisted that they bring it to her bedroom.

"I don't like the idea of her sleeping with that thing burning in her room," said Nana Rose to Ed and Leah.

"What do you mean? I slept with 'that thing' burning every night in my room for my first nine years!"

"Sparks could fly."

"No, it's very well designed," said Ed. "It's probably safer than our electric toaster."

"Well, I don't like the idea."

"Well, I do," Nana Sashie said bluntly.

"I thought it was supposed to be for the whole family?" Nana Rose persisted.

"It is. You can come up to my room for tea any time. It's easier for you to come upstairs than for me to come down."

That seemed to settle it; the samovar went to Nana Sashie's room. If people wanted a cup of tea, they had to go to her bedroom, which consequently became quite socially active.

But that first night the samovar would belong to Nana Sashie and Rache alone. At least, that was the thought in Rache's mind as she moved across the hall carpeting to Sashie's room. It was 2:30 in the morning and Rache had not even needed the alarm to wake her for this short hike toward the long journey through time, through Nana Sashie's time, to the world that might not be strictly their preserve for much longer. She stepped into the bedroom. The polished good soldier loomed before her in the night. The street lights were lawns away in the suburbs, and yet the samovar seemed lambent and luminous, as if catching the reflections from a distant mirror.

"I knew you'd come tonight."

Rache jumped in surprise. The voice sounded so young.

"Nana Sashie!"

"Who else?"

"You're awake?"

"Yes."

"How's your stomach?"

"What about my stomach?"

"The garlic didn't upset it?"

"Of course not! Stop with the stomach already! Come sit down here beside me." She patted the covers. "Quite remarkable, isn't it? With just one piece to start with, your father did an amazing job! And now he's back, the good soldier." Nana Sashie gave Rache's hand a squeeze.

Like iron filings pulled to a magnet, Rache's and Sashie's eyes were drawn to the glow of the samovar. The old eyes flickered with new color. As Nana Sashie began her story, time melted. A century bent. There was a young voice.

"We're going with him?"

A strange waxy face with dreadful eyes had melted out of the mist of the cobbler's alley. Sashie felt a stinging cuff on her ear as soon as she asked the question.

"Be quiet!" Her father's voice was sharp. He leaned forward and greeted Wolf warmly.

As Sashie saw her father's hand actually touch the other man's flesh, she felt her stomach turn, and she recoiled in horror. She sought her mother's hand, but Ida was like a statue, rigid, her eyes unseeing sockets. Through the fog came the disembodied cluckings of chickens. Sounds, even the strangest ones, took on a peculiar intimacy in the thickness of a fog, and Sashie shivered as she heard these.

"Wolf Levinson," said Joe. "My family—Sashie; my wife, Ida; my sister, Ghisa; and my father, Sol."

Wolf nodded and touched his hand to his hat in his first social gesture in twenty-five years.

"We have no time to waste, Joe." Sashie felt her mother wince at hearing her husband's name spoken by this man. "So if you will follow me, the wagon's right here. I have arranged the coops so you can get in and lie flat. Then I'm afraid after you're settled I must put them back to cover you."

"Yes. Yes, Wolf, we understand," said Joe.

"Well then, this way and we can lay out the bedclothes to make it more comfortable." There was a bustling as bundles were taken off backs and rearranged in the wagon. Sashie was busy untying her own, but she suddenly was aware of a stony, inexorable stillness directly behind her. It was as if Ida were not even breathing. Joe put down his toolbox and moved quickly to her side. He spoke gently. "Come on now, Ida." He began to untie her bundle quickly. "It's going to be all right."

"The chickens are one thing, but the devil is something else!"

"Don't be silly, Ida." But Ida did not answer.

Crawling down a temporary center aisle Wolf had made, Sashie was helping Ghisa spread the bedclothes on the floor of the wagon. As long as she kept helping Ghisa she did not have to look at or really think about the strange face with the awful eyes. But now there was trouble. She could sense it. Ida was not moving and Joe was desperate. Sashie peeked around a coop. Her mother's bedrock stance shocked her. She felt the real possibility that the escape might never begin, that they were doomed to stand here until morning, when they would be discovered. And then what? She had absolutely no idea how her father could ever move her mother onto the wagon. It would take a miracle. Sashie suddenly thought of Moses standing by the Red Sea before it parted. Next to Ida, the Red

Sea was a puddle to jump. Sashie had never seen anything as unmovable as Ida. Partially hidden by the coop, Sashie listened to the drama taking place between her parents.

"Ida, you must!" pleaded Joe.

"Who is this man?"

"Ida, he is our only chance."

"What hell has he been to?"

"Ida!" Joe swallowed hard and brought his face close to hers. "For the love of our children, get in that wagon!" What in the world was he going to do, Sashie wondered. Carry her?

"Ida, say this with me." And Joe began a soft chant: "*She'ma Y'Isoreal! Adonai Aloujanou! Adonai Echod!* Hear, O Israel! The Lord our God! The Lord is One!"

Sashie's eyes widened as she saw her mother lean on her father's arm and begin to move. As she took these first steps on the longest journey, Sashie could hear her mother whispering softly the words of the *Shema*, the Jewish statement of faith.

The blankets had been spread. Ida and Sashie stretched out in the most forward part of the wagon, each with a baby tucked in at her side. The space left between them was for Joe. At their toes were the tops of Ghisa's and Zayde Sol's heads, who were stretched out from the midsection of the wagon to the back end. Ida and Sashie settled in as best they could. With a small pillow under their heads, they had about twelve or fifteen inches clearance between their faces and the chicken coops. This seemed much more ample than Sashie had imagined. There was plenty of room to place a tier of the samovar over her face as a shield.

"This isn't bad, Mama," said Sashie, trying on the samovar face mask. "Here, try it." Sashie turned toward her mother to hand her the brass piece.

"No, I want to see," Ida said emphatically.

"So much for the samovar!" muttered Ghisa, whose voice floated up from Sashie's feet. There was no way that Sashie could see Ghisa's or Zayde Sol's face, and she found that she missed the smirk that must have punctuated her aunt's remark. She could just see her mother's face by turning her head to the side, and she could see Louie's chubby face, tucked in under her own arm and sleeping for now. Her father had arranged himself between Ida and Sashie. His head was a little forward of theirs, so he did not block their view of each other, and in order to see Joe, Ida and Sashie needed only to crane their necks and look up a bit. He quickly put a hand on each of their shoulders.

"Well, is everything as comfortable as possible here? You know, you don't need to be on your backs; you can turn over on your stomachs. Everyone all right?" Joe asked. "Ida?"

"All right." She replied flatly.

"Sashie?"

"Fine, Papa."

"Ghisa?"

"Lovely!" Darn, Sashie thought. She wished she could see Ghisa's face.

"Papa?" Joe asked.

There was a slight pause, then, "I'm alive?"

"All ready?" Wolf's face loomed at the end of the aisle.

"All set," Joe answered. His voice seemed tinged with excitement that bordered more on joy than fear.

"All right, I'll put on the last coops."

There was a great clatter and clacking as Joe dropped the first coop into the center aisle where it rested on the edges of the flanking coops. A little chunk of white night disappeared, and Sashie felt her heart beat faster. More clatter and clucks, and another piece of the night vanished. One by one the coops were dropped, and piece by piece the world above Sashie and her family was eaten up. The clucking of chickens choked the air around her, and Sashie found herself gulping for breath. Terrified of inhaling one of the white feathers that tumbled crazily through the air, she tried to screen her mouth with her scarf, but then it was harder to breathe.

"Sashie!" Her father's voice came through strong and gentle. "Look at me, Sashela." She craned her neck towards her father. "You breathe like me now. Do just what I do. First in through the nose, not too deep, then out through the mouth blowing softly. Slowly. Take your time, Sashela. There's plenty of air. And you think of nice things, like the smell of bread baking and kites flying and the first leaves of May and lighting Hanukkah candles."

"Harruh!" They heard Wolf grunt and slap the reins on the horse's back. The wagon groaned and lurched forwards, the wheels creaking, and they were on their way. Sashie thought she could count every cobblestone as the wagon rolled down the cobbler's alley. But she kept breathing just as her father had told her to and tried to think of nice things—things that now seemed rare and wondrous, like an open window on a starry summer night, a raindrop's path on glass, April branches with leaves curled tight as babies' fists.

They must be on Vaskeyevka Street. She would try and guess their route as they went. But she certainly could not see, and at this hour there were no sounds except the blizzard of cluckings that raged inches above them. She wondered if they would go by the park. And then after the park, what? She had never gone beyond the park. The Alexandra Gate of the park was the farthest perimeter of her life. Some chicken droppings splattered on her cheek, but just as disgust welled up inside Sashie a new noise split the cluckings—iron spikes hitting stone. The world above was laced with the rhythmic strikes.

"Whoa! Whoa!" She felt the wagon stop. Ghisa slid forwards a bit, her head pressing on Sashie's feet, and Sashie's head pressed against her father's arm. Louie's eyes flew open. Sashie opened her eyes as wide as she could and, staring directly into the little boy's, commanded his silence with an unblinking and fierce gaze that was intended to freeze his tongue. Quickly she reached up her sleeve for a sugar stick and popped it into his mouth. It worked, this time. Outside she could hear Wolf conversing in Russian with some men. The street was being repaired and impassable for a four-wheel vehicle. They must turn around and take Zolodievka Street. There followed a great deal of jangling and jolting shot through with Wolf's grunts and barks at the horse. Sashie felt the wagon roll backwards a few feet, then forwards. There were more barks. From the noise Sashie thought that Wolf must be off the wagon and guiding the horse around by pushing and pulling on the harness. Louie cried out once, but the sound was drowned by the tumult of the horse whinnying in protest, chickens clucking, harness jangling, wheels creaking, not to mention the string of curses and barks emanating from Wolf.

"Old man!" said one of the street workers jovially. "Watch your tongue. You know there are not just roosters aboard your wagon. I see some hens!"

The swirl of feathers seemed to freeze in the air above Sashie. She felt Ghisa grab her foot and her father's hand bite into her shoulder.

"Just joking!" She heard the man protest innocently. "Can't you take a joke, old man?"

Sashie had not heard Wolf say anything to the street worker, but she had a sense that Wolf need not say much to fill another with dread. The wagon was finally turned around. The street worker stood just by Sashie's side of the wagon now. With only the boards between them, she could hear him mutter nervously to the other, "Queer eyes!" Sashie could feel Wolf climbing into the driver's seat.

"Harruh!" he yelled. The wagon lurched forwards and clattered out of the street.

If they had to take Zolodievka Street instead of this one, it must be fairly near, and if it were fairly near, reasoned Sashie, the Alexandra Gate of the park was not that far away. Approaching the edge of her known world, Sashie felt a ripple of excitement run through her body. She remembered suddenly a book her father had shown her that had a picture of a map from long long ago, from before Columbus had discovered the new world. The map showed a world with the continents and oceans known in the early fifteenth century. At a certain distance from the land, sea serpents were drawn riding through the crests of waves, with the legend HERE BEGINNETH THE REGION OF THE DRAGONS. Except, thought Sashie, in Russia the dragons live everywhere, and she and her family were supposed to be escaping from them to the tsarless region of what angels? She was not sure. Although she herself had not dealt directly with the dragons, Sashie never once doubted their existence. One did not have to have tea with the tsar and tsarina to have his life sabotaged by them, or their ministers, or the notorious Black Hundreds, who were nothing but street thugs glorified by the tsar and given a license to kill Jews. She remembered her father's stories of the army and she had the feeling that that was not the half of it. And she would never forget the night the news came of the murder of her grandparents. She had been only three years old at the time, but she would never forget it—the hollow, stunned voice of her mother repeating over and over, "Both of them?" No, Sashie believed in these dragons, and something deep, deep inside told her that the dragon's fire had scorched Wolf. His eyes were queer because he had looked straight down the fiery throat. She wondered what it was he had seen. She would probably never know, Sashie thought, and she could certainly never ask.

Louie had finished his sugar stick and was demanding more. Sashie felt the wagon turn another corner. They must be near the Alexandra Gate. Had Columbus been forced to begin the region of the dragons with a baby wailing for more and twisting his nose, as Louie was now twisting Sashie's? "Hush, hush!" commanded everyone, but Louie would not be quiet.

"Give him another one!" hissed Ghisa from Sashie's feet. Sashie groped up her sleeve for another sugar stick. "Here," she huffed, "what do I care if you grow up to have rotten teeth!"

Ida prayed a strange prayer—that her baby boy would grow old enough to have rotten teeth. And Joe, buoyed by Sashie's relentless optimism, smiled quietly to himself and patted his daughter on the shoulder.

Sashie had fifteen sugar sticks. At this rate, she calculated, they would not last the day. "We might need the b-o-t-t-l-e." Ida and Joe weren't overjoyed at the prospect of drugging babies, but such a possibility had had to be planned for on this trip and a bottle of milk with a light sleeping draught had been prepared. Just then Sashie heard a torrent of water from a slop bucket being thrown out a high window. The chickens on the left side of the wagon forward of her sent up a loud cackle. They must have caught some of it, and then under the layer of cackles was another noise—a steamy hiss of curses from Ghisa.

There seemed to be more street noises now—shutters being opened, dogs barking, more wheels creaking, fragments of early morning talk drifting out of doorways as shopkeepers readied for trade. But where were they? It sounded nothing like the noises one would hear around the Alexandra Gate. There were not any buildings near the gate from whose windows slop buckets would be emptied. They must be beyond the gate and near the outskirts of Nikolayev, Sashie thought. As if to answer her question, there was suddenly a new sound and a new motion as the wheels of the wagon rolled from cobblestones to wood. The bass tones of the wooden planks rumbled beneath the wheels and the rush of coursing spring waters muted the manic cluckings. Even Louie, who had managed to sit up, stopped sucking on his sugar stick.

"What dat?" the baby demanded softly.

"It's the river." Sashie whispered. "We're leaving Nikolayev now."

"Oh."

"Be a good boy, Louie!" Sashie patted his knee. Louie was now starting to crawl around, exploring under the chicken coops. It seemed to keep him quiet and drain off some of his energy, so nobody tried to stop him. There wasn't far he could go.

As the wagon moved from the bridge to the dirt road, the clucks and cackles rolled up once more in a suffocating swarm. Oh, to hear water again! thought Sashie. But the liquid resonance of the flowing river was soon a memory obliterated by the cackles that seemed to bristle right inside Sashie's brain. She would go mad if she listened to the chickens another minute! She would think of a song. But she could not think of one. She would try to hear the road under the wheels. But she could not hear it. The road did, however, feel different from the cobblestone streets. It was softer. The speed seemed slower—not just slower, but thicker, Sashie thought. How can motion feel thick? It was not a bad feeling. And the noise, it wasn't noise. She caught herself. How can I hear noise, Sashie thought, above the cackles? But she did. And it was different. It wasn't noise that was reflected from hard surfaces like cobblestones, wood, and granite. It came from a deep quiet center. They were soft and sucking sounds; the sound of things being absorbed, soaked up. It's mud sounds, thought Sashie, ecstatically. "I am listening to spring mud." It was like beautiful music to Sashie.

Just above the mud but not as high as the wagon top she heard another sound. It was the whispering of a south wind blowing through winter grass. Sashie had never in her life been outside the city. She had never known the sound of the vast quietness of the country, which absorbed noise to make new sound. She lay perfectly still, listening as the country sounds bloomed around her like huge flowers.

Through the minutes and in and out of hours they slept, whispered, ate a hunk of bread or piece of potato. The babies were doing tolerably well and the sleeping draught had not yet been needed. A huge baked potato kept Louie busy for twenty minutes. A medley of whispered nursery rhymes delivered by Sashie and her father averted a near tantrum.

Sashie had just finished drawing tiny faces on both her thumb and index finger for a puppet finger show to entertain Louie when she felt Wolf slow the horse.

"Whoa!" he said.

330

The horse and the wagon stopped. Just as Wolf had begun to speak to the horse, Sashie had heard distant rapid beats, like small explosions in the earth.

"Trouble!" Wolf's voice was tight with fear. "Everybody must be quiet! It's soldiers." He paused, and Sashie thought she could hear the breath catch in his throat. "Oh, no! It's an imperial regiment!"

Then there was a timpani of cold metal as sabers and spurs jangled in the air. Sashie had managed to grab Louie and press him flat on the floor. Her father lay his leg over the little boy's kicking ones and Sashie clapped her hand over his mouth.

"Hail! In the name of their imperial majesties, the Tsar Nicholas and the Tsarina Alexandra!"

Wolf mumbled something conciliatory, but Sashie could not hear the exact words, for the only noise was that of metal clanging, leather squeaking, hooves striking the ground, animals panting, and occasional coughs. The chickens' clucking was eclipsed by the noises that accompanied the tsar's regiment of twenty on an exercise in the countryside. And beneath the chicken coops the human cargo lay in frozen terror.

"You carry chickens, I see . . ." The commander spoke. "And where are you bound for?"

"Oh, just to Borisov to deliver them for my boss to a client."

"How generous of your boss. I am sure he would not begrudge a few chickens for the tsar's regiment, and the client will never miss them."

"Lieutenant, if you please, two or three coops." Sashie heard a man jump from a horse.

"Aaaaagggg!" screamed Wolf. "Hold it!"

" 'Hold it!' You old Zhidi!" The last word hung in the air like a dagger dripping blood. "Zhidi," the abusive word for "Jew," had become quite popular with the latest wave of pogroms. Sashie trembled all over. She pressed her hand harder on Louie's mouth.

The commander spoke slowly. "You deny one of the tsar's most loyal and favored regiments a few chickens? To deny the tsar's officers is to deny the tsar, and to deny the tsar is to deny God!" the voice thundered.

"No! No! I do not deny anything to you, your . . . your excellency. It's just that the coops are in bad repair and if you carry them with you they are bound to come apart and the chickens escape. Better you take the chickens slaughtered."

"Fine. Lieutenant, skewer a few chickens then, if you will."

There was a bright flash and Sashie's breath suddenly locked in her throat. Her eyes widened in terror as she saw the

tip of a thin silver blade slice through the mesh and come within three inches of her face. Time stopped as her eyes focused on the glinting sliver of death that played above her. She could even see the scarlet sleeve of the officer's jacket. The three gold buttons blazed through a small flurry of white feathers, and the black decorative braid at the cuff was like four coiled snakes ready to strike. The silvery death dance went on raging above her face and throat. The moist still air from her half-open mouth fogged the blade tip.

"Here! I find you a fat one. Those are all skinny." The blade stilled. The silver death retreated through the slashed mesh to the world above, and Sashie fainted.

A few seconds later she came to and heard Wolf talking rapidly.

"Those are the scrawny ones. Good breeders, but no good eating. Now over here we have your scratchers."

"Scratchers?" asked the commander.

"Yeah, scratchers. They have to scratch for their food. Makes 'em tough. Stringy. They're big chickens, mind you. Weighty, but quite tough. No flavor. But here. Here in the middle we have our plumpsters—we call them plumpsters." Wolf prattled on faster than a runaway cart down Kliminsky Street on the science and technology of poultry. "With the plumpsters you get more meat per cubic centimeter than any other kind of chicken. Succulent! Juicy! You see, the plumpsters are not required to scratch for their food. And what food it is! Whole-grain bread soaked in gravy, pumpkin seeds, kasha. We Zhidi should only eat like that! The plumpsters' main job in life is eating, with an occasional stroll in a very small area. A chicken, one might say, truly fit for a tsar. Please sire, your sword. I will fetch you the plumpest of the plump-sters. Yes, a rare bird indeed!"

Sashie felt the wagon shake as Wolf pulled himself up on the side. "Kosher is quick!" She heard Wolf mutter to himself in Yiddish. In less than three minutes he had slaughtered ten chickens. Blood dripped down the center aisle onto the bed-clothes.

"Your chickens, your excellency. May you and your officers eat them in good health!"

"Your client will never miss them," came the reply.

As the spurs dug into flanks, whinnies mixed with leathery squeaks and metallic janglings filled the air. The command finally came—"Forward!"—and then the rapid explosive noises of eight hooves striking the earth as they moved off with their imperial load.

Zhidi, Sashie thought, when at last she could think again. Wolf called himself a Zhidi. How very strange that he could do this—abuse himself with this foul word even though it was done to ingratiate himself with the commander. For the first hours after the encounter with the regiment, Sashie lay in a state of total exhaustion. It was as if her nerves, her brain, and each muscle in her body had used every bit of energy avail-able. Gradually, however, she began to realize that she was alive. It was a miracle. It was as if she were a newborn baby with an older mind that could appreciate the wonder of its own birth—of being born a whole, complete human being. She tingled all over with the sheer excitement of her own liv-ing body. She touched her throat and face. She traced the gul-lies and curves of her ears. She pressed hard through all the layers of clothing and felt a rib. She took a joyous inventory of her body. Then after the miracle of survival was confirmed, she thought of Wolf and the word he had used in reference to himself. How absolutely confounding and unfathomable it was. She could not imagine ever calling herself by this horrible name, no matter what the danger was.

Sashie had stared unblinkingly as Death sliced the air just inches from her face and throat. She was sure Wolf had seen something worse, but what was it? The haunted man contained a death riddle. Sashie had been brought to the edge, but Wolf in some way had crossed over.

The fog had long ago burned off and slants of sunlight had pierced through the mesh and feather storm into the netherworld of the coops. But now the sun was at too low an angle to light the wagon, and Sashie felt a twilight chill. If she could only move more, she would feel warmer. Louie was warm as a puppy from crawling around under the coops, and though he was now sleeping, his short little body could curl up into a nice ball perfect for conserving energy. Sashie tucked him in closer to her own body to steal a little heat. Soon she drifted in and out of a troubled sleep that jolted and lurched and flashed with silver blades dripping blood. Then everything stopped and she woke up into a night-still world with her own hand fast at her throat.

"All right!" Wolf shouted. She felt him jump down from the driver's seat. "We're here."

"Thank God!"

"Am I dead or alive?"

"Or a chicken!"

"It's all right, Ida, we're here!"

"Oh, Joe!"

"Hang on, folks. I'll get the coops off in half a second." Sashie felt Wolf climb on the back end of the wagon. She heard the clatter of the first coop being removed.

"Ah!" exclaimed Ghisa with wonder as she saw the first piece of the world above. Another two coops were removed and Sashie heard Zayde Sol recite a *broche*, a prayer, upon seeing the evening again. Then another coop was removed and a square of night sky reappeared, black velvet chinked with stars. Piece by piece the sky came back and the wind, with the smell of winter grass and earth, blew across Sashie's face.

Each person had to be helped off the wagon by Wolf and, except for Louie, walked around a few feet by him until their legs and back regained their strength. Sashie needed Wolf's arm only for a couple of steps. Almost immediately she was off on her own trying out her new legs. First she tried walking a few meters, but the night was so warm, the air so gentle, and the field so vast that Sashie felt she must dance, leap, fly through this startling country. Under the starry dome of the Russian night Sashie whirled and jumped. Her head thrown back, she watched the stars spin and smelled the thawing earth and listened to the wind songs in the grass.

Ghisa too was soon running and skipping in jerky little circles around a moonlit tree stump. The babies squealed and Ida and Joe said soft prayers of thanksgiving and laughed gently with each other in the night. And Zayde Sol said more *broches*—*broches* for seeing stars again, *broches* for seeing the moon, *broches* for seeing a baby walk, and *broches* for seeing a granddaughter dance.

THE LAND I LOST:
ADVENTURES OF
A BOY IN VIETNAM
from the book by Huynh Quang Nhuong
illustrated by Allen Eitzen

I was born on the central highlands of Vietnam in a small hamlet on a riverbank that had a deep jungle on one side and a chain of high mountains on the other. Across the river, rice fields stretched to the slopes of another chain of mountains.

There were fifty houses in our hamlet, scattered along the river or propped against the mountainsides. The houses were made of bamboo and covered with coconut leaves, and each was surrounded by a deep trench to protect it from wild animals or thieves. The only way to enter a house was to walk across a "monkey bridge"—a single bamboo stick that spanned the trench. At night we pulled the bridges into our houses and were safe.

There were no shops or marketplaces in our hamlet. If we needed supplies—medicine, cloth, soaps, or candles—we had to cross over the mountains and travel to a town nearby. We used the river mainly for traveling to distant hamlets, but it also provided us with plenty of fish.

During the six-month rainy season, nearly all of us helped plant and cultivate fields of rice, sweet potatoes, Indian mustard, eggplant, tomatoes, hot peppers, and corn. But during the dry season, we became hunters and turned to the jungle.

Wild animals played a very large part in our lives. There were four animals we feared the most: the tiger, the lone wild hog, the crocodile, and the horse snake. Tigers were always trying to steal cattle.

Sometimes, however, when a tiger became old and slow it became a maneater. But a lone wild hog was even more dangerous than a tiger. It attacked every creature in sight, even when it had no need for food. Or it did crazy things, such as charging into the hamlet in broad daylight, ready to kill or to be killed.

The river had different dangers: crocodiles. But of all the animals, the most hated and feared was the huge horse snake. It was sneaky and attacked people and cattle just for the joy of killing. It would either crush its victim to death or poison it with a bite.

Like all farmers' children in the hamlet, I started working at the age of six. My seven sisters helped by working in the kitchen, weeding the garden, gathering eggs, or taking water to the cattle. I looked after the family herd of water buffaloes. Someone always had to be with the herd because no matter how carefully a water buffalo was trained, it always was ready to nibble young rice plants when no one was looking. Sometimes, too, I fished for the family while I guarded the herd, for there were plenty of fish in the flooded rice fields during the rainy season.

I was twelve years old when I made my first trip to the jungle with my father. I learned how to track game, how to recognize useful roots, how to distinguish edible mushrooms from poisonous ones. I learned that if birds, raccoons, squirrels, or monkeys had eaten the fruits of certain trees, then those fruits were not poisonous. Often they were not delicious, but they could calm a man's hunger and thirst.

My father, like most of the villagers, was a farmer and a hunter, depending upon the season. But he also had a college education, so in the evenings he helped to teach other children in our hamlet, for it was too small to afford a professional schoolteacher.

My mother managed the house, but during the harvest season she could be found in the fields, helping my father get the crops home; and as the wife of a hunter she knew how to dress and nurse a wound and took good care of her husband and his hunting dogs.

I went to the lowlands to study for a while because I wanted to follow my father as a teacher when I grew up. I always planned to return to my hamlet to live the rest of my life there. But war disrupted my dreams. The land I love was lost to me forever.

These stories are my memories. . . .

OPERA AND KARATE

When she was eighty years old grandmother was still quite strong. She could use her own teeth to eat corn on the cob or to chew on sugar plants to extract juice from them. Every two days she walked for more than an hour to reach the marketplace, carrying a heavy load of food with her, and then spent another hour walking back home. And even though she was quite old, traces of her beauty still lingered on: Her hands, her feet, her face revealed that she had been an attractive young woman. Nor did time do much damage to the youthful spirit of my grandmother.

One of her great passions was theater, and this passion never diminished with age. No matter how busy she was, she never missed a show when there was a group of actors in

town. If no actors visited our hamlet for several months, she would organize her own show in which she was the manager, the producer, and the young leading lady, all at the same time.

My grandmother's own plays were always melodramas inspired by books she had read and by what she had seen on the stage. She always chose her favorite grandson to play the role of the hero, who would, without fail, marry the heroine at the end and live happily ever after. And when my sisters would tell her that she was getting too old to play the role of the young heroine anymore, my grandmother merely replied: "Anybody can play this role if she's young at heart."

When I was a little boy my grandmother often took me to see the opera. She knew Chinese mythology by heart, and the opera was often a dramatization of this mythology. On one special occasion, during the Lunar New Year celebrations—

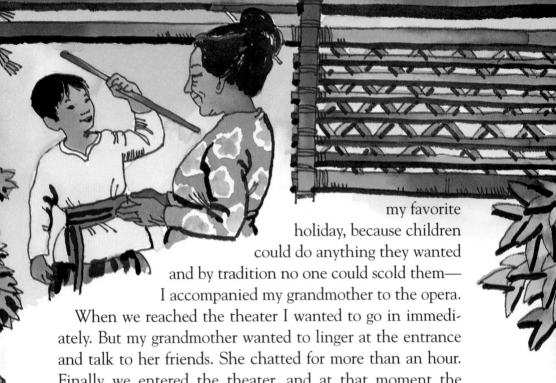

my favorite
holiday, because children
could do anything they wanted
and by tradition no one could scold them—
I accompanied my grandmother to the opera.
When we reached the theater I wanted to go in immediately. But my grandmother wanted to linger at the entrance
and talk to her friends. She chatted for more than an hour.
Finally we entered the theater, and at that moment the
"Faithful One" was onstage, singing sadly. The "Faithful One"
is a common character in Chinese opera. He could be a good
minister, or a valiant general, or someone who loved and
served his king faithfully. But in the end he is unjustly perse-
cuted by the king, whose opinion of him has been changed by
the lies of the "Flatterer," another standard character.

When my grandmother saw the "Faithful One" onstage she
looked upset and gave a great sigh. I was too interested in
what was happening to ask her the reason, and we spent the
next five hours watching the rest of the opera. Sometimes I
cried because my grandmother cried at the pitiful situation of
the "Faithful One." Sometimes I became as angry as my
grandmother did at the wickedness of the "Flatterer."

When we went home that night my grandmother was quite
sad. She told my mother that she would have bad luck in the

following year because when we entered the theater, the "Faithful One" was onstage. I was puzzled. I told my grandmother that she was confused. It would be a good year for us because we saw the good guy first. But my mother said, "No, son. The 'Faithful One' always is in trouble and it takes him many years to vindicate himself. Our next year is going to be like one of his bad years."

So, according to my mother's and grandmother's logic, we would have been much better off in the new year if we had been lucky enough to see the villain first!

My grandmother had married a man whom she loved with all her heart, but who was totally different from her. My grandfather was very shy, never laughed loudly, and always spoke very softly. And physically he was not as strong as my grandmother. But he excused his lack of physical strength by saying that he was a "scholar."

About three months after their marriage, my grandparents were in a restaurant and a rascal began to insult my grandfather because he looked weak and had a pretty wife. At first he just made insulting remarks, such as, "Hey! Wet chicken! This is no place for a weakling!"

My grandfather wanted to leave the restaurant even though he and my grandmother had not yet finished their meal. But my grandmother pulled his shirt sleeve and signaled him to remain seated. She continued to eat and looked as if nothing had happened.

Tired of yelling insults without any result, the rascal got up from his table, moved over to my grandparents' table, and

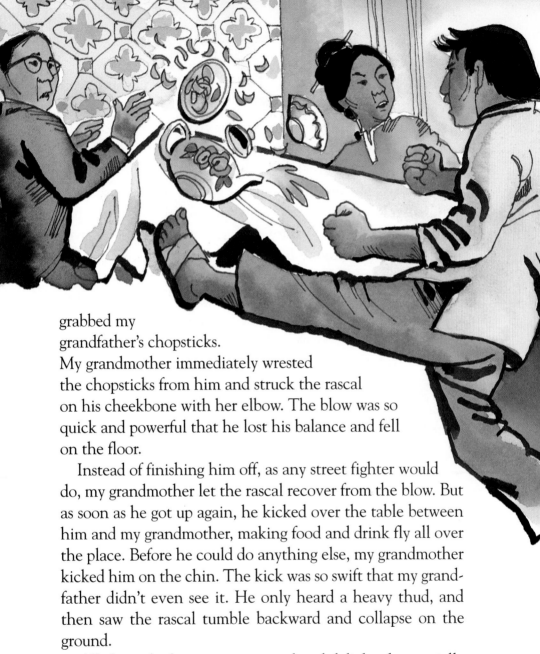

grabbed my
grandfather's chopsticks.
My grandmother immediately wrested
the chopsticks from him and struck the rascal
on his cheekbone with her elbow. The blow was so
quick and powerful that he lost his balance and fell
on the floor.

Instead of finishing him off, as any street fighter would
do, my grandmother let the rascal recover from the blow. But
as soon as he got up again, he kicked over the table between
him and my grandmother, making food and drink fly all over
the place. Before he could do anything else, my grandmother
kicked him on the chin. The kick was so swift that my grandfather didn't even see it. He only heard a heavy thud, and
then saw the rascal tumble backward and collapse on the
ground.

All the onlookers were surprised and delighted, especially
the owner of the restaurant. Apparently the rascal, one of the
best karate fighters of our area, came to this restaurant every

day and left without paying for his food or drink, but the owner was too afraid to confront him.

While the rascal's friends tried to revive him, everyone else surrounded my grandmother and asked her who had taught her karate. She said, "Who else? My husband!"

After the fight at the restaurant people assumed that my grandfather knew karate very well but refused to use it for fear of killing someone. In reality, my grandmother had received special training in karate from my great-great uncle from the time she was eight years old.

Anyway, after that incident, my grandfather never had to worry again. Anytime he had some business downtown, people treated him very well. And whenever anyone happened to bump into him on the street, they bowed to my grandfather in a very respectful way.

One morning my grandmother wanted me to go outside with her. We climbed a little hill that looked over the whole area, and when we got to the top she looked at the rice field below, the mountain on the horizon, and especially at the river. As a young girl she had often brought her herd of water buffaloes to the river to drink while she swam with the other children of the village. Then we visited the graveyard where her husband and some of her children were buried. She touched her husband's tombstone and said, "Dear, I will join you soon." And then we walked back to the garden and she gazed at the fruit trees her husband had planted, a new one for each time she had given birth to a child. Finally, before we left the garden my sister joined us, and the two of them fed a few ducks swimming in the pond.

That evening my grandmother did not eat much of her dinner. After dinner she combed her hair and put on her best dress. We thought that she was going to go out again, but instead she went to her bed room and told us that she didn't want to be disturbed.

The family dog seemed to sense something was amiss, for he kept looking anxiously at everybody and whined from time to time. At midnight my mother went to my grandmother's room and found that she had died, with her eyes shut, as if she were sleeping normally.

It took me a long time to get used to the reality that my grandmother had passed away. Wherever I was, in the house, in the garden, out on the fields, her face always appeared so clearly to me. And even now, many years later, I still have the feeling that my last conversation with her has happened only a few days before.

PARMELE

from CHILDTIMES: A THREE-GENERATION
MEMOIR by Eloise Greenfield
and Lessie Jones Little

E very summer we took a trip down home. Down home
was Parmele.

To get ready for our trip, Daddy would spend days
working on our old car, putting it in shape to go on the road,
and Mama would wash and iron all of our clothes. Then
everything would be packed in the tan leather suitcase and
the black cardboard suitcase, and we'd be ready to go.

Mama and Daddy would sit in the front with Vedie in
Mama's lap, and Wilbur, Gerald, and I sat in the back with our
legs on top of the suitcases. This was before cars had trunks.
Or radios. Or air conditioners or heaters. And there were no
superhighways. The speed limit was forty-five miles an hour,
and we went thirty-five to keep from straining the car.

It was an eight-hour trip to Norfolk, Virginia, where we
always went first. Grandma Pattie Ridley Jones and Grandpa
had moved there by that time, and we'd spend about a week
with them, then go on to Parmele for another week.

On the road, I played peek-a-boo with Vedie between her
naps. Or my brothers and I would count all the cars on the
road. We'd say, "There go one! That's twenty-two. There go
another one!" And we'd read out loud the rhymes on the red

signs advertising Burma shaving cream, and wave at people sitting on their porches, and argue with each other until one of us got real mad and real loud and Mama told us we were giving her the jimjams and to be quiet.

One thing that we saw on the road frightened me. Chain gangs. We saw them often, the lines of black men in their black-and-white-striped jail suits, chained by their ankles and watched over, as they repaired the roads, by white men with guns.

I wasn't afraid of the men, and I didn't think about maybe getting shot. But for a reason I didn't understand, I was afraid of the whole thing. Those bent-over striped backs, the sharp points of the picks the men swung, the sound of the picks hitting the concrete, the sight of men with long guns, pacing. It scared me.

After a few miles, that scared feeling would fade away, and I'd start to have fun again, or I might take a nap, and it always seemed as if days had passed before we finally crossed the line into Parmele.

By the time of my visits there, only a few trains were still passing through. My Parmele wasn't a train town or a mill town. It was a quiet town. Chinaberry trees and pump water and tree swings and figs and fat, pulpy grapes on the vine. People saying, "hey" instead of "hi," the way they did in Washington, *hey-ey*, sending their voices up, then down, softly, singing it through their noses. Parmele was me running from the chickens when I was little, riding around the yard in a goat-pulled cart, sitting on the porch and letting people going by in their cars wave at me, reading in the rocking chair, taking long walks to the gas station for soda pop with the children of Mama's and Daddy's childtime friends. Parmele was uncles and aunts and cousins. And Granny. And Pa.

They were Daddy's parents, Mack and Williamann Little. Black people in Parmele called them Mr. Mack and Miss Williamann. White people called them Uncle Mack and Ain' Williamann.

Granny was thin and whitehaired. She kept snuff tucked inside her bottom lip and wore aprons over her long dresses. I remember her most bending over the collards in her garden or feeding the chickens. She used to sew leftover material from my dresses into her patchwork quilts. She used to make apple jelly and green tomato pickles. Anything her grandchildren wanted, she wanted them to have.

And so did Pa.

"Leave the children alone," he used to tell mamas and daddies. "They ain't doing nothing."

Pa was a sharecropper. He worked in the fields, farming the land for the white man who owned it, and got paid in a share of the crops he raised. Along with that, he had almost always had some kind of little business going, even when Daddy was a boy—a meat market, an icehouse, a cleaner's, a grocery store.

Long before I was born, Pa had been a member of the Marcus Garvey group that used to meet in Parmele on Sunday afternoons. It was one of thousands of branches of the United Negro Improvement Association headed by Marcus Garvey. They met to talk about the beauty and strength of blackness, and to plan the return of black people to Africa.

I didn't think my grandfather was afraid of anything except the frogs that came out of the mud-filled ditches at night and flopped across the yard, and he knew plenty of names to call

Eloise Greenfield stands at the far right of this photograph taken at Parmele in 1941. With her are her grandfather, her mother, her grandmother, Wilbur, Vedie, and Gerald.

them. The thumb on his right hand looked like a little bald-headed man. The top joint had been cut off in a farm accident, and he had put it in a jar of preserving liquid that stayed on the front-room mantel. I never got tired of looking at it.

Children hung around Pa, nieces and nephews and neighbors, listening to his stories, giggling at his jokes. Some nights there would be just us—Wilbur, Gerald, and me, with our grandfather—sitting on the porch where the only light was that of the stars and the nearest house was a long way down the road. He'd tell scary stories, and get really tickled when we got scared. He swore his ghost stories were true.

"One night," he'd say, "me and my brother John was coming 'cross that field over yonder." He'd make his arm tremble and point toward the woods across the highway. "And we commence to hearing this strange sound. Ummmmm-*umph!* Ummmmm-*umph!* And we looked up and saw this . . . this *haint!*"

He'd twist his face and narrow his eyes in horror as he stared out into the darkness, and I could just feel all those haints hovering behind us, daring us to turn around and run for the door.

Sometimes Pa would stop right in the middle of a story.

"Then what happened, Pa?" one of us would ask.

"Oh, I left after that," he'd say, and he'd laugh. Then we'd laugh, small nervous laughs, wanting to believe that it had all been just a joke.

Every year when it was time for us to leave, a sudden change would come over Pa. One minute he'd be challenging Daddy to a foot race that never took place, and the next minute he was weak and sick, trying to get us to stay. He didn't think he would live to see us the following summer, he'd say. At breakfast he'd begin the blessing with, "Lord, I sure do thank You for allowing me to see my family one last time before You call me home," and he'd pray a long, sad prayer that brought tears to our eyes.

But finally, when nothing worked, Pa would give up and help Daddy load the car with suitcases and with sacks of fresh corn and peanuts. There'd be hugs and kisses and more tears, and then we'd drive away, leaving him and Granny standing on the side of the road, waving, waving, waving, getting smaller and smaller, until they blended into one and disappeared.

Pa never liked to leave home. Granny came to visit us a few times over the years, but Pa always made an excuse. He couldn't get away right then, he had too much work to do, or something. One year, though, he had to come. He'd had a stroke, and Mama and Daddy brought him to Washington to take care of him. The stroke had damaged his body and his mind, so that he didn't understand much of what was going on around him, but he knew he wasn't where he wanted to be. Mama would take him for a walk and he'd ask people on the street, "Which way is Parmele?"

My grandfather never got back to Parmele. He lived in Washington for eighteen months, and then, in 1951, at the age of seventy-eight, he died.

MEET ELOISE GREENFIELD, AUTHOR
This selection from Childtimes *was written by Eloise Greenfield. Her grandmother, Patty Ridley Jones, and mother, Lessie Jones Little, wrote other parts of the book. Each of the three women tells about the times in which she grew up and the things she remembers from her childhood.*

In the preface to this book, the authors talk about family heritage: "This book is about family. Kinsfolk touching across the centuries, walking with one hand clasping the hands of those who have gone before, the other hand reaching back for those who will come after. . . .

"We came, one behind the other, to our childtimes— grandmother, mother, daughter—just three marchers in a procession that stretches long and wide. Stretches across the ocean to the continent of Africa, back to great-grandmothers and great-grandfathers and great-greats and great-great-greats, and on and on, all the way back to the beginning of human life on earth. Stretches outward to sisters and brothers and aunts and uncles and nephews and nieces and cousins. A long, wide, family procession with thousands of marchers. We are just three."

BIBLIOGRAPHY

Going Home by Nicholasa Mohr. Eleven-year-old Felita, a New Yorker, spends the summer with relatives in Puerto Rico.

Grandparents' Houses: Poems about Grandparents, selected by Corrine Streich. You'll enjoy the poems in this book and the illustrations by Lillian Hoban that go with them.

The Great Ancestor Hunt: The Fun of Finding Out Who You Are by Lila Perl. This book might help you start your search for your roots.

Homesick: My Own Story by Jean Fritz. Growing up in China, Jean Fritz was intensely aware of her American heritage.

Immigrant Kids by Russell Freedman. Photographs from the early 1900s help tell about the experience of immigrants from Europe.

A *Jar of Dreams* by Yoshiko Uchida. A Japanese-American girl growing up in California in the 1930s comes to appreciate her heritage when her aunt visits from Japan.

Joel: Growing Up a Farm Man by Patricia Demuth. Thirteen-year-old Joel is already working at the job he hopes to do all of his life: caring for crops and animals, and managing the business of farming.

Pueblo Storyteller by Diane Hoyt-Goldsmith. A young Native-American girl living in the Cochiti Pueblo near Santa Fe, New Mexico, tells about her people's customs and about the storyteller dolls her grandmother makes.

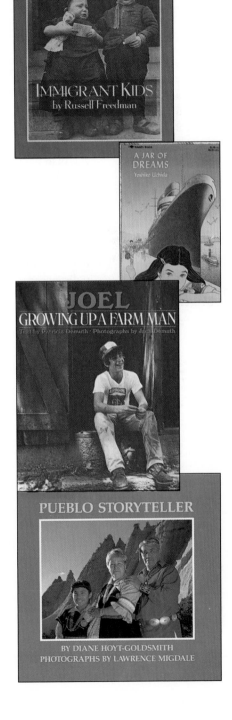

GLOSSARY

a as in at	o as in ox	ou as in out	ch as in chair
ā as in late	ō as in rose	u as in up	hw as in which
â as in care	ô as in bought	ûr as in turn;	ng as in ring
ä as in father	and raw	germ, learn,	sh as in shop
e as in set	oi as in coin	firm, work	th as in thin
ē as in me	o͝o as in book	ə as in about,	t͟h as in there
i as in it	o͞o as in too	chicken, pencil,	zh as in treasure
ī as in kite	or as in form	cannon, circus	

The mark (´) is placed after a syllable with a heavy accent,
as in **chicken** (chik´ ən).
The mark (ˊ) after a syllable shows a lighter accent,
as in **disappear** (dis´ ə pēr´).

acceleration (ak sel´ ə rā´ shən) n. An increase in speed.

accumulation (ə kyo͞o´ myə lā´ shən) n. A piled-up mass.

accuracy (ak´ yər ə sē) n. Exactness; correctness.

adobe (ə dō´ bē) n. Sun-dried brick.

agate (ag´ it) n. A stone with swirls or stripes of several colors.

alien (āl´ yən) adj. From another world. —n. A being from another world.

align (ə līn´) v. To place in a straight line.

alignment (ə līn´ mənt) n. The arrangement of things in a straight line.

amiss (ə mis´) adv. Wrong; not as expected.

ample (am´ pəl) adj. More than enough.

anguish (ang´ gwish) n. Great distress; pain.

anomaly (ə nom´ ə lē) n. Something that is different from the usual arrangement.

anticipate (an tis´ ə pāt´) v. To know or feel in advance.

application (ap´ li kā´ shən) *n.* A form that is filled out to request something.

apprehension (ap´ ri hen´ shən) *n.* Fear.

arc (ärk) *v.* To move in a curved line. —*n.* A curve.

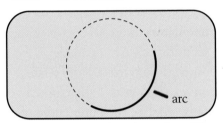

archaeology (är´ kē ol´ ə jē) *n.* The scientific study of people of the past by digging up things they left behind.

arthritis (är thrī´ tis) *n.* A disease of inflamed joints, often associated with advanced age.

ascend (ə send´) *v.* To climb up; to rise.

astronomical (as´ trə nom´ i kəl) *adj.* Having to do with the study of the stars and planets.

astronomy (ə stron´ ə mē) *n.* The scientific study of stars and planets.

automated (ôt´ ə mā´ təd) *adj.* Automatic; run by machines.

avert (ə vûrt´) *v.* To avoid.

bedrock (bed´ rok´) *n.* Solid rock.

blemish (blem´ ish) *n.* A stain; a defect.

brooch (brōch) *n.* A decorated pin or clasp worn as jewelry.

cairn (kârn) *n.* A pile of stones left as a landmark or a monument.

calculation (kal´ kyə lā´ shən) *n.* 1. Counting, computing, or figuring. 2. The result of counting, computing, or figuring.

calibrate (kal´ ə brāt´) *v.* To measure by marking off equal amounts.

caribou (kar´ ə bōō´) *n.* A reindeer.

catechism (kat´ i kiz´ əm) *n.* Instruction in the principles of a Christian religion.

chartreuse (shär trōōz´) *n.* A yellowish-green color.

chiffon (shi fon´) *n.* A soft, see-through material made of silk, nylon, or rayon.

Pronunciation Key: at; lāte; câre; fäther; set; mē; it; kīte; ox; rōse; ô in bought; coin; bŏŏk; tōō; form; out; up; tûrn; ə sound in about, chicken, pencil, cannon, circus; **chair; hw** in **which; ring; shop; thin;** **th**ere; **zh** in treasure.

circuit (sûr´ kit) *n.* The path of an electrical current. **short circuit:** A condition in which something gets in the way of the path of an electrical current and causes either too much electricity or not enough.

civilization (siv´ ə lə zā´ shən) *n.* A culture, society, or group of human beings who have developed education, trade, agriculture, science, art, government, and so on.

clamber (klam´ bər) *v.* To climb with difficulty.

classic (klas´ ik) *n.* A book of high quality. **The classics:** The literature of ancient Greece and Rome.

cobbler (kob´ lər) *n.* A person who repairs shoes and boots.

commence (kə mens´) *v.* To begin.

compensate (kom´ pən sāt´) *v.* To make up for; to offset.

complication (kom´ pli kā´ shən) *n.* Something that makes a situation more difficult.

composition (kom´ pə zish´ ən) *n.* What something is made of.

concave (kon kāv´) *adj.* Curved inward; hollow; like the inner curve of a contact lens.

conciliatory (kən sil´ ē ə tor´ ē) *adj.* Causing peace to be made.

confront (kən frunt´) *v.* To face.

convex (kon veks´) *adj.* Curved outward; like the outer curve of a contact lens.

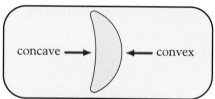

countenance (koun´ tn əns) *n.* A person's face or expression.

cringe (krinj) *v.* To back away from something unpleasant.

cultivate (kul´ tə vāt´) *v.* To till the ground; to grow crops.

cylindrical (si lin´ dri kəl) *adj.* Having a shape like a roller or a short tube.

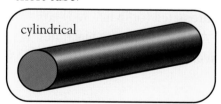

deduction (di duk´ shən) *n.* A fact or conclusion figured out by reasoning.

defect (dē´ fekt) *n.* A fault; a flaw.

deign (dān) *v.* To lower oneself; to stoop to do something that is beneath one.

delicacy (del´ i kə sē) *n.* A tasty morsel of food; a special food that is rare or expensive.

delicatessen (del´ i kə tes´ ən) *n.* A shop selling prepared foods, such as cooked meats and salads.

demolish (di mol´ ish) *v.* To do away with.

descendant (di sen´ dənt) *n.* Anyone born from a particular family line.

detract (di trakt´) *v.* To take away from.

diffusion (di fyoo´ zhən) *n.* A spreading out or scattering.

dike (dīk) *n.* A bank or wall of earth built to hold back the water of a river or the sea.

diminish (di min´ ish) *v.* To decrease; to lessen; to get smaller.

din (din) *n.* Clamor; uproar; racket.

disability (dis´ ə bil´ i tē) *n.* Anything that takes away a person's ability to do something or puts a person at a disadvantage.

disembodied (dis´ em bod´ ēd) *adj.* Without a body.

dissipate (dis´ ə pāt´) *v.* To scatter.

dramatization (dram´ ə tə zā´ shən) *n.* An acting out of a story.

draught (draft) *n. chiefly British.* A liquid that is drunk; a dose.

dubious (doo´ bē əs) *adj.* Doubtful; uncertain.

eclipse (i klips´) *n.* A darkening of the sun or the moon. —*v.* To darken; to cover over.

economize (i kon´ ə mīz´) *v.* To reduce expenses; to save money.

ecstatically (ek stat´ ik lē) *adv.* With great joy.

eddy (ed´ ē) *n.* A current of air or water that moves in circles. —*v.* To whirl into circle shapes.

edible (ed´ ə bəl) *adj.* Eatable; wholesome.

elusive (i loo´ siv) *adj.* Hard to get.

emphatically (em fat´ ik lē) *adv.* With spoken firmness or force.

enthrall (en thrôl´) *v.* To hold someone's interest; to charm.

equinox (ē´ kwə noks´) *n.* The two times of the year when day and night are equal in length.

eternal (i tûr´ nl) *adj.* Everlasting; always; endless.

Pronunciation Key: at; lāte; câre; fäther; set; mē; it; kīte; ox; rōse; ô in bought; coin; bŏŏk; tōō; form; out; up; tûrn; ə sound in about, chicken, pencil, cannon, circus; chair; hw in which; ring; shop; thin; ŧhere; zh in treasure.

ferocious (fə rō´ shəs) *adj.* Full of fury.

ferocity (fə ros´ i tē) *n.* Wildness; fury; savageness.

frigid (frij´ id) *adj.* Very cold.

geometry (jē om´ i trē) *n.* A mathematical science concerned with the measurement of lines, surfaces, and solids.

geyser (gī´ zər) *n.* A hot-water fountain; a jet of hot water that shoots from the ground.

geyser

gingerly (jin´ jər lē) *adv.* Cautiously; warily.

granite (gran´ it) *n.* A very hard stone used for building, usually gray or pink.

gravitational (grav´ i tā´ shən əl) *adj.* Having to do with the force of gravity, which pulls all bodies toward the center of the earth.

hamlet (ham´ lit) *n.* A small village.

hesitation (hez´ i tā´ shən) *n.* A slight pause.

hover (huv´ ər) *v.* To hang in the air.

hue (hyōō) *n.* A tint; a shade of color.

hypnotic (hip not´ ik) *adj.* Causing sleep.

illuminate (i lōō´ mə nāt´) *v.* To throw light upon; to shine upon.

immortality (im´ or tal´ i tē) *n.* The state of living forever.

impact (im´ pakt) *n.* An influence or effect.

inexorable (in ek´ sər ə bəl) *adj.* Absolute; unyielding.

inferno (in fûr´ nō) *n.* A place of extreme, intense heat.

infrared (in´ fra red´) *adj.* Having to do with the invisible rays that are closest to the red end of the visible light spectrum. See illustration of **ultraviolet.**

ingenious (in jēn´ yəs) *adj.* Clever; skillful.

ingratiate (in grā´ shē āt´) *v.* To put oneself in the good graces of others.

inquisitive (in kwiz´ i tiv) *adj.* Curious.

intelligible (in tel´ i jə bəl) *adj.* Clear; understandable.

interpreter (in tûr´ pri tər) *n.* Someone who changes words from one language into another language.

interstellar (in´ tər stel´ ər) *adj.* Between the stars. Interstellar space is the part of outer space that is beyond our solar system.

intimacy (in´ tə mə sē) *n.* A closeness.

intimidate (in tim´ i dāt´) *v.* To frighten; to awe.

intricate (in´ tri kit) *adj.* Tangled; complicated.

invalid (in´ və lid) *n.* A sick person.

kaleidoscope (kə lī´ də skōp´) *n.* A constantly changing pattern.

kasha (kä´ shə) *n.* A soft food made from a grain, usually buckwheat.

kayak (kī´ ak) *n.* A light Eskimo canoe having a wooden or bone framework and covered with skins.

kayak

lambent (lam´ bənt) *adj.* Glowing softly.

laminated (lam´ ə nā´ tid) *adj.* Covered with a thin layer of material.

learned (lûrnd) *v.* Past tense of **learn**: To gain new knowledge or skill. —*adj.* (lûr´ nid) Educated.

lubricant (lōō´ bri kənt) *n.* A substance such as oil or grease that makes machine parts slippery, thus making the parts move easily.

lull (lul) *n.* A period of reduced noise or violence.

luminescent (lōō´ mə nes´ ənt) *adj.* Giving off light; shining.

magnification (mag´ nə fi kā´ shən) *n.* The amount of enlargement possible; the amount something is enlarged.

Pronunciation Key: at; lāte; câre;
fäther; set; mē; it; kīte; ox; rōse; ô in
bought; coin; bŏŏk; tōō; form; out; up;
tûrn; ə sound in about, chicken, pencil,
cannon, circus; chair; hw in which;
ring; shop; thin; ŧhere; zh in treasure.

maneuver (mə nōō´ vər) *n.* A
movement that calls for planning
and skill.

manic (man´ ik) *adj.* Overly
excited; crazed.

manual (man´ yōō əl) *adj.* Done by
hand.

manufacture (man´ yə fak´ chər) *v.*
To make.

Maya or **Mayan** (mä´ yə) or (mä´
yən) *n.* A member of a people
who built a civilization in Mexico
and Central America before the
time of Columbus. **Mayan** *adj.*
Having to do with the civilization
of the Mayas.

meditate (med´ i tāt´) *v.* To think
deeply; to contemplate.

medley (med´ lē) *n.* A mixture; a
jumble.

melodrama (mel´ ə drä´ mə) *n.* A
play that exaggerates emotions
and encourages the audience to be
sympathetic.

merge (mûrj) *v.* To be mixed
together.

miaow (mē ou´) *n.* Meow; the
sound a cat makes. —*v.* To meow;
to make the sound a cat makes.

mill (mil) *n.* A factory.

miniature (min´ ē ə chər) *adj.* A
small-sized model of something.

mother-of-pearl (muŧh´ ər uv
pûrl´) *n.* A hard, shiny,
multicolored substance found
inside some mollusk shells.

motor (mō´ tər) *adj.* Having to do
with moving one's body.

myriad (mir´ ē əd) *n.* An immense
number; many.

mystified (mis´ tə fīd´) *adj.*
Bewildered; baffled; puzzled.

mythology (mi thol´ ə jē) *n.* A
collection of legends or fables.

netherworld (neŧh´ ər wûrld´) *n.*
The region below the ground;
hell.

notwithstanding (not´ wiŧh stan´
ding) *prep.* In spite of.

nuclear reaction (nōō´ klē ər rē ak´
shən) *n.* A process in which the
centers or cores of atoms are
changed.

obligingly (ə blī´ jing lē) *adv.*
Helpfully.

obliterate (ə blit′ ə rāt′) *v.* To destroy completely; to rub out; to erase.

oblong (ob′ lông′) *adj.* Being longer than it is wide.

obscure (əb skyŏŏr′) *adj.* Not well known. —*v.* To hide; to cover up.

observatory (əb zûr′ və tor′ē) *n.* A place that is designed for astronomers to study the stars.

observatory

obstacle (ob′ stə kəl) *n.* A hindrance; something that gets in the way.

optical (op′ ti kəl) *adj.* Having to do with sight.

optimism (op′ tə miz′ əm) *n.* The belief that everything will happen for the best.

organic (or gan′ ik) *adj.* Produced by living things; was once alive.

orientation (or′ ē ən tā′ shən) *n.* A person's or object's position in relation to something else.

oval (ō′ vəl) *adj.* Egg-shaped.

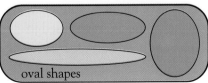
oval shapes

paramount (par′ ə mount′) *adj.* Supreme; chief in importance.

passion (pash′ ən) *n.* A strong liking or enthusiasm for something.

pauper (pô′ pər) *n.* A very poor person.

peculiarity (pi kyŏŏ′ lē ar′ i tē) *n.* A strange or unusual feature.

perimeter (pə rim′ i tər) *n.* The distance around the boundary of something.

persecute (pûr′ si kyŏŏt′) *v.* To torment; to oppress; to treat badly.

perspective (pər spek′ tiv) *n.* A way of looking at things in relation to each other.

pickerel (pik′ ər əl) *n.* A freshwater fish that is in the pike family.

pig iron (pig′ ī′ ərn) *n.* A rectangular block of iron ready to be made into steel or other types of iron.

plateau (pla tō′) *n.* A tract of high, flat land; a tableland.

plot (plot) *v.* To mark on a chart or a map.

pogrom (pə grum′) *n.* An organized attack on Jews in Russia in the late 1800s. Pogroms were encouraged by the Russian government at that time.

Pronunciation Key: at; lāte; câre; fäther; set; mē; it; kīte; ox; rōse; ô in bought; coin; bŏŏk; tōō; form; out; up; tûrn; ə sound in about, chicken, pencil, cannon, circus; chair; hw in which; ring; shop; thin; ŧħere; zh in treasure.

portal (por´ tl) *n.* A little room or entryway with a connecting door.

portly (port´ lē) *adj.* Stout; chubby.

precarious (pri kâr´ ē əs) *adj.* Uncertain; doubtful.

precaution (pri kô´ shən) *n.* Care taken beforehand.

primary (prī´ mer ē) *adj.* Main.

ptarmigan (tär´ mi gən) *n.* A bird also known as a grouse.

pun (pun) *n.* A joke made by using words that sound almost the same but have different meanings.

qualification (kwol´ ə fi kā´ shən) *n.* A legal authority; a license; a degree.

ramshackle (ram´ shak´ əl) *adj.* Tumbledown; shaky.

rancid (ran´ sid) *adj.* Stale; unpleasant.

recoil (ri koil´) *v.* To spring back from.

reflect (ri flekt´) *v.* To throw back rays of light.

refracting (ri frak´ ting) *adj.* Passing through an object and changing direction, as a light ray passing into a lens at one angle and coming out at a different angle.

renounce (ri nouns´) *v.* To give up; to reject.

resolve (ri zolv´) *v.* To decide; to have as a purpose.

resonance (rez´ ə nəns) *n.* Richness of sound; echoing.

revelation (rev´ ə lā´ shən) *n.* A discovery of something new.

reverie (rev´ ə rē) *n.* A daydream.

rigid (rij´ id) *adj.* Stiff; unbending.

ritual (rich´ ōō əl) *n.* A ceremony of worship; an act always performed on certain occasions.

rivulet (riv´ yə lit) *n.* A small stream of water.

rotate (rō´ tāt) *v.* To revolve; to turn around; to spin.

saber (sā´ bər) *n.* A heavy sword with a curved blade.

sabotage (sab´ ə täzh´) *v.* To damage purposely.

samovar (sam´ ə vär´) *n.* A decorative metal container with a spigot, or faucet, often used in Russia to heat water for tea.

scowl (skoul) *v.* To frown; to glare.

seclude (si klo͞od´) *v.* To keep away from others.

self-sufficiency (self´ sə fish´ ən sē) *n.* The ability to live on one's own; the ability to supply all one's own food, shelter, clothing, and other needs.

sensor (sen´ sor) *n.* A device that can identify such things as light, sound, or temperature, and can send a signal telling what has been identified.

shamefaced (shām´ fāst´) *adj.* Embarrassed.

sharecropper (shâr´ krop´ ər) *n.* A farmer who gives part of the crop as rent to the owner of the land.

shinny (shin´ ē) *v.* To climb up something by grasping it with one's legs.

skulk (skulk) *v.* To sneak.

solar system (sō´ lər sis´ təm) *n.* The sun and all the planets and other bodies that revolve around it.

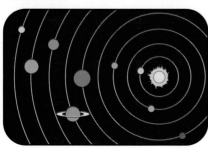
solar system

solstice (sol´ stis) *n.* The day of the year when the sun appears the farthest north and the day when it appears the farthest south in the sky.

spawn (spôn) *v.* To lay eggs and deposit them in the water.

spew (spyo͞o) *v.* To pour out; to squirt out.

sphere (sfēr) *n.* A ball; a globe.

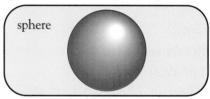
sphere

spire (spīr) *n.* A tall, pointed cone built on top of a tower; a steeple.

stabilization (stā´ bə lə zā´ shən) *n.* The act of making something hold steady.

stance (stans) *n.* A person's mental position on a subject.

Stonehenge (stōn´ henj) *n.* A group of large stones in England placed in circular formations around 3,500 years ago, possibly as an astronomical calendar.

Stonehenge

Pronunciation Key: at; lāte; câre; fäther; set; mē; it; kīte; ox; rōse; ô in bought; coin; bŏŏk; tōō; form; out; up; tûrn; ə sound in about, chicken, pencil, cannon, circus; chair; hw in which; ring; shop; thin; there; zh in treasure.

stroke (strōk) *n.* A sudden attack of illness caused by a blocked or broken blood vessel in or leading to the brain.

succulent (suk´ yə lənt) *adj.* Juicy; tasty.

suffocate (suf´ ə kāt´) *v.* To smother; to choke.

surplus (sûr´ plus) *n.* An amount more than is needed; an extra amount.

swivel chair (swiv´ əl châr´) *n.* A chair which has a seat that turns around.

synchronize (sing´ krə nīz´) *v.* To move together at the same rate.

tempo (tem´ pō) *n.* The rate or pattern of activity.

tidal flat (tīd´ l flat´) *n.* A flat area of land that is sometimes covered by tidal waters.

timpani (tim´ pə nē) *n.* A set of drums.

translate (trans lāt´) *v.* To change something from one language into another.

translucent (trans lōō´ sənt) *adj.* Hard to see through. Light is visible but objects cannot be seen clearly.

transmit (trans mit´) *v.* To send; to communicate; to pass something.

transmitter (trans mit´ ər) *n.* A device that sends out television or radio signals.

trench (trench) *n.* A ditch; a long, narrow channel cut in the earth.

tribute (trib´ yōōt) *n.* Praise, honor, or gifts given to show respect or to show thanks.

tripod (trī´ pod) *n.* A three-legged table or stand.

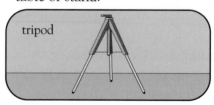
tripod

tsar (zär) *n.* An emperor of Russia before 1918.

tsarina (zä rē´ nə) *n.* An empress of Russia before 1918.

tumult (tōō´ mult) *n.* A great disorder; an uproar.

tundra (tun´ drə) *n.* A large, treeless plain in the arctic regions.

turbulent (tûr´ byə lənt) *adj.* Fierce; violent; wild.

ultraviolet (ul´ trə vī´ ə lit) *adj.* Having to do with an invisible form of light. Ultraviolet rays are found just beyond the violet end of the visible spectrum.

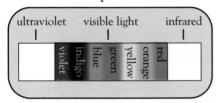

unison (yōō´ nə sən) *n.* Behaving the same way at the same time. **in unison** *idiom.* Two or more people saying or doing the same thing at the same time.

unquenchably (un kwench´ ə blē) *adv.* Endlessly; in a persistent way.

vacuum (vak´ yōōm) *n.* A space with no air. A perfect vacuum is not possible; even in space there are some atoms and molecules of gas and radiation, although they are thinly scattered.

valiant (val´ yənt) *adj.* Brave; fearless.

velocity (və los´ i tē) *n.* Speed.

vermillion (vər mil´ yən) *adj.* Bright red.

vindicate (vin´ di kāt´) *v.* To prove innocent.

water buffalo (wô´ tər buf´ ə lō´) *n.* A kind of oxen with large curved horns and bluish-black hide. Water buffaloes are trained to work in rice fields in Asia.

water buffalo

wince (wins) *v.* To flinch; to start back from.

YWCA Young Women's Christian Association.

continued from page 5

Morrow Junior Books, a division of William Morrow and Co., Inc.: *Stars* by Seymour Simon, text copyright © 1986 by Seymour Simon.

Penguin Books Canada Limited: An excerpt entitled "A Real Job" from *Little by Little* by Jean Little, copyright © 1987 by Jean Little.

Penguin USA: An excerpt from *The Night Journey* by Kathryn Lasky, illustrated by Trina Schart Hyman, text copyright © 1981 by Kathryn Lasky, illustrations copyright © 1981 by Trina Schart Hyman.

Marian Reiner, for the author, and Holiday House, for the illustrator: "Sun" and "Secrets" from *Space Songs* by Myra Cohn Livingston, illustrated by Leonard Everett Fisher, text copyright © 1988 by Myra Cohn Livingston, illustrations copyright © 1988 by Leonard Everett Fisher, published by Holiday House.

Walker and Co., 720 Fifth Avenue, New York, NY 10019: An excerpt from *How Did We Find Out the Earth Is Round?* by Isaac Asimov, copyright © 1972 by Isaac Asimov.

Photography
83   Guelph Daily Mercury
113   B. & C. Alexander/Black Star
139   AP/Wide World
309   K. Yep
311   Jean Weisinger

Diagrams
147, 148, 149 Accurate Art, Inc.

COLOPHON

This book has been designed in the classic style to emphasize our commitment to classic literature. The typeface, Goudy Old Style, was drawn in 1915 by Frederic W. Goudy, who based it on fifteenth-century Italian letterforms.

The art has been drawn to reflect the golden age of children's book illustration and its recent rebirth in the work of innovative artists of today. This book was designed by John Grandits. Composition, electronic page makeup, and photo and art management were provided by The Chestnut House Group, Inc.